PENGUIN

ARKANA

THE VOICE OF KAHLIL GIBRAN

Poet, philosopher and artist, Kahlil Gibran was born near Mount Lebanon. The millions of Arabic-speaking peoples familiar with his writings in that language consider him the genius of his age, but his fame and influence spread far beyond the Near East. His writings have been translated into more than twenty languages and his drawings and paintings have been exhibited all over the world. *The Prophet*, his masterpiece of religious inspiration, and its companion, *The Garden of the Prophet*, are also published in Penguin Arkana. Kahlil Gibran was for many years the leader of a Lebanese literary circle in New York, where he died in 1931.

Robin Waterfield was born in 1952. He graduated from Manchester University in 1974 and went on to research ancient Greek philosophy at King's College, Cambridge. He has been a university lecturer (at Newcastle upon Tyne and St Andrews), and a copy editor and a commissioning editor for Penguin Books. In between, and currently, he makes a living as a self-employed writer and consultant editor. His publications range from academic articles to children's fiction. He has translated various Greek philosophical texts, including several for Penguin Classics: Xenophon's *Conversations of Socrates*, Plutarch's *Essays*, Plato's *Philebus* and *Theaetetus* and (in Plato's *Early Socratic Diaologues*) *Hippias Major*, *Hippias Minor* and *Euthydemus*.

The Prophet, read by Renu Setna, and *The Garden of the Prophet*, read by Nadim Sawalha, are available as Penguin Audiobooks.

ROBIN WATERFIELD

The Voice of Kahlil Gibran:
An Anthology

ARKANA
PENGUIN BOOKS

ARKANA

Published by the Penguin Group
Penguin Books Ltd, 27 Wrights Lane, London w8 5tz, England
Penguin Books USA Inc., 375 Hudson Street, New York, New York 10014, USA
Penguin Books Australia Ltd, Ringwood, Victoria, Australia
Penguin Books Canada Ltd, 10 Alcorn Avenue, Toronto, Ontario, Canada m4v 3b2
Penguin Books (nz) Ltd, 182–190 Wairau Road, Auckland 10, New Zealand

Penguin Books Ltd, Registered Offices: Harmondsworth, Middlesex, England

This selection first published 1995
3 5 7 9 10 8 6 4 2

The moral right of the editor has been asserted

Set in 10.5/13.5 pt Monotype Bembo
Typeset by Datix International Limited, Bungay, Suffolk
Printed in England by Clays Ltd, St Ives plc

CONTENTS

v

PART TWO
Complete Short Stories

PART THREE
Aphorisms and Extracts

PART FOUR Prophecies:
Extracts from *The Prophet* and
The Garden of the Prophet

PART FIVE Christ and Christianity:
Extracts from *Jesus the Son of Man*

INTRODUCTION

Kahlil Gibran is one of the world's most famous and popular writers, with book sales numbering in many millions in over twenty languages, and increasing every year. In the English-speaking world, his best-known book by far is *The Prophet*, but he wrote a number of other books, which deserve to be better known (for full details, see the bibliography on pp. xvii–xx). *The Prophet* may be his greatest work, but it is devoted to a single character, Almustafa the Prophet, who therefore speaks more or less with a single voice. However, the voice of Kahlil Gibran himself is capable of far more variation. He can speak with great anger and bitterness, as well as the optimism and compassion for which he is better known. In short, he explores the full range of emotions – and does so in both prose and poetry, and in a variety of writing styles, from the deliberately archaic and biblical to the pithy and colloquial. He writes Aesopian fables with neat psychological twists, if they are taken to describe internal attitudes rather than external events; he writes poignant short stories; he writes homilies and quasi-political poems, aphorisms and gnomes in both prose and poetry. The point of any given piece is often immediately accessible and obvious, but invariably there are also hidden layers and resonances waiting to surprise us on a second or third reading.

Despite his great fame, and despite the fact that he is Lebanon's most eminent literary export to the West, and despite the fact that the details of his life have been well chronicled on a number of occasions, there still remain some uncertainties and grey areas. How, for instance, to start with basics, should one spell and pronounce the English version of his name? The answer is given on the front cover of this book, as of all recent editions of his books and biographies. For Gibran himself accepted this Anglicization of his name from what would, more strictly, have been Gibran Khalil Gibran – with the extra forename and the aspirated K. Yet the British Library persists, in the majority of its records, in calling him Jabran, which has the benefit only of alerting the English-speaking world to the fact that the G in ´Gibran is not hard, but soft. And some writers prefer the authentic-looking versions Djabran or Joubran.

Then again, although everyone agrees on the outline of his life, the exact dates given in one biography do not always quite match those given in another. But here, briefly, are the broad details of his life. He was born on 6 January 1883 in the town of Bsharri, which lies, as the crow flies, some forty miles north-north-east of Beirut in what is now Lebanon, although in those days it was part of Syria, which was in turn part of the Turkish empire. He was the first child of the marriage between Khalil ben Gibran, a poor cattle-dealer and tax-collector, and his wife Kamila (who already had a son, Peter, from a previous marriage). Two daughters were to follow in later years: Mariana and Sultana.

Gibran was brought up in the faith of his parents, who were Christians of the Maronite Church, which is the main

Christian Church of Lebanon, and is peculiar to Lebanon. Named after a Syrian monk of the late fourth and early fifth centuries, it has since the early thirteenth century had the distinction of being 'uniate' – that is, it is an Eastern Orthodox Church which acknowledges papal supremacy while retaining the Orthodox liturgy and practices. It may be worth mentioning that in 1860, well within Gibran's parents' lifetimes, 16,000 Maronites were killed and 100,000 driven from their homes by Islamic Druse persecution.

In 1895, at Peter's instigation, the family emigrated to Boston in the United States, but without the father, who stayed behind to take care of business. Gibran himself, however, returned to Lebanon a couple of years later to complete his education on home territory rather than in the States. He also edited there a literary and philosophical magazine entitled *El Hakikat* (*The Truth*). A few years later, he left Lebanon for good (although he was not to know it at the time), first spending two years in Paris studying art at the Academy Julian (and moving in artistic and literary circles), and then rejoining the rest of his family in Boston in 1903. Apart from travels, and in particular two years back in Paris (1908–10), Gibran was to spend the rest of his life in the USA, first in Boston and then from 1911 in New York (which he both loved and loathed). He died young, after prolonged illness, on 10 April 1931.

What were the early influences on his life? First, there was his love of the Lebanese countryside, with its valleys, mountains and famous cedars. Then there was his Christian faith, although that became, as we shall see, somewhat unorthodox. Finally, there was his mother, Kamila. Gibran seems to have inherited almost nothing, in terms of character,

from his father, but a great deal from his artistically in-
clined mother. And women were to remain throughout
his life his single most powerful source of inspiration. In
1928, in a letter to May Ziadeh, he wrote: 'I am indebted
for all that I call "I" to women, ever since I was an infant.
Women opened the windows of my eyes and the doors of
my spirit. Had it not been for the woman–mother, the
woman–sister, and the woman–friend, I would have been
sleeping among those who seek the tranquillity of the
world with their snoring.' And apart from his mother,
women were always to play an important part in Gibran's
life and work; his relationships with women such as Mary
Haskell and Barbara Young, in particular, have been well
documented in the biographies. It is worth mentioning,
however, as a curiosity, that Gibran's epistolary love affair
with May Ziadeh, a young Lebanese admirer of his living
in Egypt, whom he never met, bears comparison with the
more famous such love affair between Helene Hanff and
Frank Doel, as revealed in Hanff's book *84 Charing Cross
Road*.

These influences on Gibran will be more or less apparent
in the anthology that follows. The same goes for two other
formative incidents. First, at some point in his late teens,
Gibran clearly fell desperately in love with a young woman
whose father, under social pressure, married her to someone
else. Biographers differ over the name of the girl, and
whether Gibran was in Beirut or Bsharri at the time, and
to what extent the affair is accurately portrayed in his
novella *Broken Wings*, but these details do not matter for
our present purposes. What is important is that the affair
opened Gibran's eyes to the supreme importance of love in
the world. He would already have been taught in church

that God is Love, but from now on this became a living, experiential fact for him, not an abstraction. Love was truth, beauty, God, everything. Nor was this love, for Gibran, only the love of God for man (or vice versa); it lives fully in the love a human lover has for his or her soul mate. Time and again in his stories, Gibran returns to the power and importance of love; combined with his unorthodox belief in reincarnation, more than one story tells of love surviving over the centuries until it could meet its fulfilment. However, he also remained aware of the rarity of true love, and believed that this scarceness was due as much as anything to the fact that true love is dangerous and revolutionary: it shatters the wall of social conventions.

There must, of course, have been many unknown formative influences on Gibran in his early years and later in life, but one more is worth mentioning here. What recalled him to Boston from Paris in 1903 was a series of tragedies. His brother Peter wrote to tell him that his sister Sultana had died of tuberculosis, and that his mother was seriously ill with the same disease. Gibran arrived in Boston, but within a few weeks Peter himself died, also of tuberculosis, before Gibran's beloved mother succumbed three months later. And so Gibran remained throughout his life keenly aware not just of the fragility of life, but also of the fact that the experience of sorrow and the striving for joy are the two poles within which the whole of a person's life is lived and out of which are born all of his or her hopes and fears and, in short, all the characteristics of his or her individuality. An almost Buddhist sense of suffering pervades a great deal of Gibran's work. Even love brings suffering – but suffering also brings the possibility of self-realization.

Another event, which would undoubtedly have embittered most people, but which simply taught the Prophet of Lebanon more about the role of sadness, was his enforced exile from Lebanon. This came about as a direct result of the publication of his first book, *Spirits Rebellious*, which was written during his first visit to Paris in the opening years of this century, and was published in Arabic in 1903. In a series of three short stories, Gibran revealed himself as a champion of freedom – of freedom against enslavement by tyrants, subjection to convention, and oppression by the materialistic demands of a Church which could be more concerned with filling its coffers than with saving souls, and which failed to understand that Jesus came for the common people, not to establish a wealthy and worldly institution. Reaction was swift. Instead of perceiving the justness of his assertions, both the Turkish government and the Maronite Church pronounced an anathema on him that was little short of exile and excommunication and copies of the book were burnt in public in Beirut. The harshness of this punishment certainly did not induce Gibran to change his mind. Throughout his life, his writings return to the tyranny of the rich over the poor, and of the clergy over the general populace, and contrast them with the freedom of a simple life – a life which has seen through the emptiness of worldly standards and possessions – and with the liberating power of a sincere, personal religion. And throughout his life he championed the course of true love even when it flies in the face of society's rules.

Although the decree of exile was rescinded in 1908, Gibran chose never to return. The loss of Lebanon remains a theme in his letters, right up to the end, but he had emotional ties to North America by then. He had friends and a career there. In particular, he was the centre of a literary circle of expatriate Lebanese writers, the most famous of whom, after himself, was Mikhail Naimy, who wrote (among other books) *The Book of Mirdad* (most recent edition: Penguin Books, 1993). They called their group Arrabitah, which is Arabic for The Pen-Bond, and it rapidly became famous throughout the Arab world.

I do not want to say more about the influences on Gibran, and therefore about his philosophy. I hope that the anthology that follows is representative; if so, the reader will gather something of Gibran's views. When I embarked on this anthology, I thought I might be able to divide all of it into sections: 'On Man', 'On Religion', 'On Love', 'On Lebanon', et cetera. But this proved to be impossible. Gibran's thoughts defy easy categorization (although the attempt has often been made). He was not a systematic thinker, but a philosopher of the people: he writes easily and openly, for everyone to read. He writes without jargon, but with great depth of meaning and conviction, and often with penetrating insight.

Having said that the anthology is intended to be representative, I have to qualify this statement. Some of his works are, in the nature of their genre, hard to excerpt. So the reader will find few or no extracts here from either of his short poetic dialogues (*The Earth Gods*, *The Procession*), or from his letters, or from his plays (*Lazarus and His Beloved*, and others found in collections of his short pieces). However, I feel that even so the anthology is not unfair. Gibran's fame rests on, and the vast majority of his work consists of, short pieces. Even his longer books (which still rarely extend to over a hundred pages) are frequently no more than collections of shorter pieces, or a variety of meditations on different subjects put into the mouth of a single spokesman (such as Almustafa the Prophet in *The Prophet* and *The Garden of the Prophet*, or the madman or the wanderer in the books with those titles). And it is precisely such short pieces, or extracts from them, which predominate in this anthology.

However, in one respect no literary anthology can hope to represent the full scope of Gibran's work. As well as being a master of the word, Gibran was also a consummate artist, whose works have often, and justly, been compared with those of William Blake. The original editions of his books are invariably accompanied by his wistful and ethereal drawings and paintings. These books should be consulted to help a reader round off his or her impressions of Gibran.

BIBLIOGRAPHY AND
ABBREVIATIONS

Works by Kahlil Gibran in English

WORKS ORIGINALLY WRITTEN IN ARABIC

1903: *Spirits Rebellious*. This contains three short stories: 'Madame Rose Hanie', 'The Cry of the Graves', and 'Khalil the Heretic'. The translation used in this anthology is by A.R. Ferris in *1 T* (see below).

1912: *The Broken Wings*. Novella. The translation used in this anthology is by A.R. Ferris in *2 T* (see below).

1914: *A Tear and a Smile* or *Tears and Laughter*. Short poems and prose poems, variously translated. The translations used in this anthology are by H.M. Nahmad, A. Ghareeb or A.R. Ferris (see below), according to preference.

1918: *The Procession*. A poetic dialogue. Translated by G. Kheirallah (New York: Philosophical Library, 1958). Unrepresented in this anthology, but also available in the translation by A.R. Ferris (see below).

Many of Gibran's early Arabic poems, essays, prose poems, short plays and short stories, whether or not they were included in any of the four books just listed, have appeared in various anthologies. These pad out the usual bibliographies of Gibran's work and make it look rather daunting, but in fact there is a great deal of overlap between these anthologies. This is not always easy to see, because different translators have given the pieces different titles: some reflections entitled 'Of Love and Equality' in one collection may appear as 'My Friend' in another. Anyway, here is a list of such anthologies.

(a) Translated by A.R. Ferris: *Secrets of the Heart* (New York: Philosophical Library, 1947)

· *Tears and Laughter* (New York: Philosophical Library, 1948)

The Voice of the Master (New York: Citadel Press, 1958)

Spiritual Sayings (New York: Citadel Press, 1962) [Abbreviated as SS]

Thoughts and Meditations (New York: Citadel Press, 1962)

Almost all of the pieces translated in these books by A.R. Ferris are also collected in either *A Treasury of Kahlil Gibran* (London: William Heinemann, 1974) or *A Second Treasury of Kahlil Gibran* (London: William Heinemann, 1992). Since these books are the most easily available in the UK, then for the convenience of readers they have been used in preference to the individual editions listed above, except in the case of *Spiritual Sayings* (SS), which is not included in these collections. The first Treasury is abbreviated in this anthology as 1T, but the second (2T) is not paginated consecutively, and is therefore referred to by those of its separate sections which are represented in this book: *The Broken Wings* is BW; *The Voice of the Master* is VM; *Thoughts and Meditations* is TM.

(b) Translated by A. Ghareeb: *Prose Poems* (New York: Alfred A. Knopf, Inc., 1934) [Abbreviated as PP]

(c) Translated by H.M. Nahmad: *Nymphs of the Valley* (New York: Alfred A. Knopf, Inc., 1947) [Abbreviated as NV]

A Tear and a Smile (New York: Alfred A. Knopf, Inc., 1950) [Abbreviated as *TS*]

(d) Translated by J. Sheban: *Mirrors of the Soul* (New York: Philosophical Library, 1965). This is mainly a biography and analysis of Gibran, but also contains some translations. It is reprinted in *A Third Treasury of Kahlil Gibran* (London: William Heinemann, 1993), along with a collection of Sheban's translations of Gibran's aphorisms. Unrepresented in this anthology.

WORKS ORIGINALLY WRITTEN IN ENGLISH

1918: *The Madman: His Parables and Poems* (New York: Alfred A. Knopf, Inc.) [Abbreviated as *M*]

1920: *The Forerunner* (New York: Alfred A. Knopf, Inc.) Fables, parables and poems. Included complete in this anthology.

1923: *The Prophet* (New York: Alfred A. Knopf, Inc.) Homilies on various topics. [Abbreviated as *P*]

1926: *Sand and Foam: A Book of Aphorisms* (New York: Alfred A. Knopf, Inc.) [Abbreviated as *SF*]

1928: *Jesus the Son of Man* (New York: Alfred A. Knopf, Inc.) Gibran's longest book, it consists of seventy-nine short, fictional impressions of Jesus, put into the mouths of characters from the Bible or from that period of history, and often drawing on the words of the Bible. [Abbreviated as *JSM*]

1929: *Lazarus and His Beloved* (New York: Alfred A. Knopf, Inc.) A short play expressing mystical Christianity. Unrepresented in this anthology.

Then the following were published posthumously:

1931: *The Earth Gods* (New York: Alfred A. Knopf, Inc.) A short poetic dialogue between three deities. [Abbreviated as *EG*]

1932: *The Wanderer* (New York: Alfred A. Knopf, Inc.) Fifty short stories, fables and parables. [Abbreviated as *W*]

1933: *The Garden of the Prophet* (New York: Alfred A. Knopf, Inc.) Further homilies by the Prophet on a variety of topics. [Abbreviated as *GP*]

LETTERS

A Self-portrait, translated by A.R. Ferris (New York: Citadel Press, 1959). Letters to his closest friends – Mikhail Naimy, May Ziadeh, et cetera. Unrepresented in this anthology.

Beloved Prophet: The Love Letters of Kahlil Gibran and Mary Haskell (New York: Alfred A. Knopf, Inc., 1972). Unrepresented in this anthology.

A Selection of Books about Kahlil Gibran

J.P. Ghougassian, *Kahlil Gibran: Wings of Thought*, in *A Third Treasury of Kahlil Gibran* (London: William Heinemann, 1993)

J. and K. Gibran, *Kahlil Gibran: His Life and World* (Los Angeles: Interlink Publishers, Inc., 1991)

M. Naimy, *Kahlil Gibran: A Biography* (New York: Philosophical Library, 1950)

J. Sheban, *Mirrors of the Soul* (New York: Philosophical Library, 1965)

B. Young, *This Man from Lebanon* (New York: Alfred A. Knopf, Inc., 1970)

ACKNOWLEDGEMENTS

The publishers would also like to thank Dover Publications, Inc., New York for use of the decorative borders and devices, which are taken from *Alphabets and Ornaments* by Ernst Lehner.

Grateful acknowledgement is made to Reed Consumer Books Ltd for permission to reprint the following extracts from copyright works:

From *A Treasury of Kahlil Gibran*, edited by Martin L. Wolf, translated from the Arabic by Anthony Rizcallah Ferris, published by William Heinemann Ltd;

From *The Broken Wings*, translated by Anthony Rizcallah Ferris, published by William Heinemann Ltd;

From *Spiritual Sayings of Kahlil Gibran*, translated by Anthony Rizcallah Ferris, published by William Heinemann Ltd;

From *Thoughts and Meditations*, translated by Anthony Rizcallah Ferris, published by William Heinemann Ltd;

From *The Voice of the Master*, translated by Anthony Rizcallah Ferris, published by William Heinemann Ltd.

PART ONE

The Forerunner

Half of what I say is meaningless; but I say it so
that the other half may reach you.

Sand and Foam, 14

THE FORERUNNER

You are your own forerunner, and the towers you have builded are but the foundation of your giant-self. And that self too shall be a foundation.

And I too am my own forerunner, for the long shadow stretching before me at sunrise shall gather under my feet at the noon hour. Yet another sunrise shall lay another shadow before me, and that also shall be gathered at another noon.

Always have we been our own forerunners, and always shall we be. And all that we have gathered and shall gather shall be but seeds for fields yet unploughed. We are the fields and the ploughmen, the gatherers and the gathered.

When you were a wandering desire in the mist, I too was there, a wandering desire. Then we sought one another, and out of our eagerness dreams were born. And dreams were time limitless, and dreams were space without measure.

And when you were a silent word upon life's quivering lips, I too was there, another silent word. Then life uttered us and we came down the years throbbing with memories of yesterday and with longing for tomorrow, for yesterday was death conquered and tomorrow was birth pursued.

And now we are in God's hands. You are a sun in His right hand and I an earth in His left hand. Yet you are not more, shining, than I, shone upon.

And we, sun and earth, are but the beginning of a greater sun and a greater earth. And always shall we be the beginning.

You are your own forerunner, you the stranger passing by the gate of my garden.

And I too am my own forerunner, though I sit in the shadows of my trees and seem motionless.

GOD'S FOOL

Once there came from the desert to the great city of Sharia a man who was a dreamer, and he had naught but his garment and a staff.

And as he walked through the streets he gazed with awe and wonder at the temples and towers and palaces, for the city of Sharia was of surpassing beauty. And he spoke often to the passers-by, questioning them about their city – but they understood not his language, nor he their language.

At the noon hour he stopped before a vast inn. It was built of yellow marble, and people were going in and coming out unhindered.

'This must be a shrine,' he said to himself, and he too went in. But what was his surprise to find himself in a hall of great splendour and a large company of men and women seated about many tables. They were eating and drinking and listening to the musicians.

'Nay,' said the dreamer. 'This is no worshipping. It must be a feast given by the prince to the people, in celebration of a great event.'

At that moment a man, whom he took to be the slave of the prince, approached him, and bade him be seated. And he was served with meat and wine and most excellent sweets.

When he was satisfied, the dreamer rose to depart. At the door he was stopped by a large man magnificently arrayed.

'Surely this is the prince himself,' said the dreamer in his heart, and he bowed to him and thanked him.

Then the large man said in the language of the city:

'Sir, you have not paid for your dinner.' And the dreamer did not understand, and again thanked him heartily. Then the large man bethought him, and he looked more closely upon the dreamer. And he saw that he was a stranger, clad in but a poor garment, and that indeed he had not wherewith to pay for his meal. Then the large man clapped his hands and called — and there came four watchmen of the city. And they listened to the large man. Then they took the dreamer between them, and they were two on each side of him. And the dreamer noted the ceremoniousness of their dress and of their manner and he looked upon them with delight.

'These,' said he, 'are men of distinction.'

And they walked all together until they came to the House of Judgement and they entered.

The dreamer saw before him, seated upon a throne, a venerable man with flowing beard, robed majestically. And he thought he was the king. And he rejoiced to be brought before him.

Now the watchmen related to the judge, who was the venerable man, the charge against the dreamer; and the judge appointed two advocates, one to present the charge and the other to defend the stranger. And the advocates rose, the one after the other, and delivered each his argument. And the dreamer thought himself to be listening to addresses of welcome, and his heart filled with gratitude to the king and the prince for all that was done for him.

Then sentence was passed upon the dreamer, that upon a tablet hung about his neck his crime should be written, and that he should ride through the city on a naked horse, with a trumpeter and a drummer before him. And the sentence was carried out forthwith.

Now as the dreamer rode through the city upon the naked horse, with the trumpeter and the drummer before him, the inhabitants of the city came running forth at the sound of the noise, and when they saw him they laughed one and all, and the children ran after him in companies from street to street. And the dreamer's heart was filled with ecstasy, and his eyes shone upon them. For to him the tablet was a sign of the king's blessing and the procession was in his honour.

Now as he rode, he saw among the crowd a man who was from the desert like himself and his heart swelled with joy, and he cried out to him with a shout:

'Friend! Friend! Where are we? What city of the heart's desire is this? What race of lavish hosts, who feast the chance guest in their palaces, whose princes companion him, whose king hangs a token upon his breast and opens to him the hospitality of a city descended from heaven?'

And he who was also of the desert replied not. He only smiled and slightly shook his head. And the procession passed on.

And the dreamer's face was uplifted and his eyes were overflowing with light.

LOVE

They say the jackal and the mole
Drink from the selfsame stream
Where the lion comes to drink.

And they say the eagle and the vulture
Dig their beaks into the same carcass,
And are at peace, one with the other,
In the presence of the dead thing.

O love, whose lordly hand
Has bridled my desires,
And raised my hunger and my thirst
To dignity and pride,
Let not the strong in me and the constant
Eat the bread or drink the wine
That tempt my weaker self.
Let me rather starve,
And let my heart parch with thirst,
And let me die and perish,
Ere I stretch my hand
To a cup you did not fill,
Or a bowl you did not bless.

THE KING-HERMIT

They told me that in a forest among the mountains lives a young man in solitude who once was a king of a vast country beyond the Two Rivers. And they also said that he, of his own will, had left his throne and the land of his glory and come to dwell in the wilderness.

And I said, 'I would seek that man, and learn the secret of his heart; for he who renounces a kingdom must needs be greater than a kingdom.'

On that very day I went to the forest where he dwells. And I found him sitting under a white cypress, and in his hand a reed as if it were a sceptre. And I greeted him even as I would greet a king. And he turned to me and said gently, 'What would you in this forest of serenity? Seek you a lost self in the green shadows, or is it a home-coming in your twilight?'

And I answered, 'I sought but you – for I fain would know that which made you leave a kingdom for a forest.'

And he said, 'Brief is my story, for sudden was the bursting of the bubble. It happened thus: one day as I sat at a window in my palace, my chamberlain and an envoy from a foreign land were walking in my garden. And as they approached my window, the lord chamberlain was speaking of himself and saying, "I am like the king; I have a thirst for strong wine and a hunger for all games of chance. And like my lord the king I have storms of temper." And the lord chamberlain and the envoy disappeared among the trees. But in a few minutes they returned, and this time the lord chamberlain was speaking of me, and he was saying, "My lord the king is like myself – a good marksman; and like me he loves music and bathes thrice a day."'

After a moment he added, 'On the eve of that day I left my palace with but my garment, for I would no longer be ruler over those who assume my vices and attribute to me their virtues.'

And I said, 'This is indeed a wonder, and passing strange.'

And he said, 'Nay, my friend, you knocked at the gate of my silences and received but a trifle. For who would not leave a kingdom for a forest where the seasons sing and dance ceaselessly? Many are those who have given their kingdom for less than solitude and the sweet fellowship of aloneness. Countless are the eagles who descend from the upper air to live with moles that they may know the secrets of the earth. There are those who renounce the kingdom of dreams that they may not seem distant from the dreamless. And those who renounce the kingdom of nakedness and cover their souls that others may not be ashamed in beholding truth uncovered and beauty unveiled. And greater yet than all of these is he who renounces the kingdom of sorrow that he may not seem proud and vainglorious.'

Then rising he leaned upon his reed and said, 'Go now to the great city and sit at its gate and watch all those who enter into it and those who go out. And see that you find him who, though born a king, is without kingdom; and him who though ruled in flesh rules in spirit – though neither he nor his subjects know this; and him also who but seems to rule yet is in truth slave of his own slaves.'

After he had said these things he smiled on me, and there were a thousand dawns upon his lips. Then he turned and walked away into the heart of the forest.

And I returned to the city, and I sat at its gate to watch the passers-by even as he had told me. And from that day to this numberless are the kings whose shadows have passed over me and few are the subjects over whom my shadow has passed.

THE LION'S DAUGHTER

Four slaves stood fanning an old queen who was asleep upon her throne. And she was snoring. And upon the queen's lap a cat lay purring and gazing lazily at the slaves.

The first slave spoke, and said, 'How ugly this old woman is in her sleep. See her mouth droop; and she breathes as if the devil were choking her.'

Then the cat said, purring, 'Not half so ugly in her sleep as you in your waking slavery.'

And the second slave said, 'You would think sleep would smooth her wrinkles instead of deepening them. She must be dreaming of something evil.'

And the cat purred, 'Would that you might sleep also and dream of your freedom.'

And the third slave said, 'Perhaps she is seeing the procession of all those that she has slain.'

And the cat purred, 'Aye, she sees the procession of your forefathers and your descendants.'

And the fourth slave said, 'It is all very well to talk about her, but it does not make me less weary of standing and fanning.'

And the cat purred, 'You shall be fanning to all eternity; for as it is on earth so it is in heaven.'

At this moment the old queen nodded in her sleep, and her crown fell to the floor.

And one of the slaves said, 'That is a bad omen.'

And the cat purred, 'The bad omen of one is the good omen of another.'

And the second slave said, 'What if she should wake, and find her crown fallen! She would surely slay us.'

And the cat purred, 'Daily from your birth she has slain you and you know it not.'

And the third slave said, 'Yes, she would slay us and she would call it making sacrifice to the gods.'

And the cat purred, 'Only the weak are sacrificed to the gods.'

And the fourth slave silenced the others, and softly he picked up the crown and replaced it, without waking her, on the old queen's head.

And the cat purred, 'Only a slave restores a crown that has fallen.'

And after a while the old queen woke, and she looked about her and yawned. Then she said, 'Methought I dreamed, and I saw four caterpillars chased by a scorpion around the trunk of an ancient oak tree. I like not my dream.'

Then she closed her eyes and went to sleep again. And she snored. And the four slaves went on fanning her.

And the cat purred, 'Fan on, fan on, stupids. You fan but the fire that consumes you.'

TYRANNY

Thus sings the she-dragon that guards the seven caves by the sea:

'My mate shall come riding on the waves. His thundering roar shall fill the earth with fear, and the flames of his nostrils shall set the sky afire. At the eclipse of the moon we shall be wedded, and at the eclipse of the sun I shall give birth to a Saint George, who shall slay me.'

Thus sings the she-dragon that guards the seven caves by the sea.

THE SAINT

In my youth I once visited a saint in his silent grove beyond the hills; and as we were conversing upon the nature of virtue a brigand came limping wearily up the ridge. When he reached the grove he knelt down before the saint and said, 'O saint, I would be comforted! My sins are heavy upon me.'

And the saint replied, 'My sins, too, are heavy upon me.'

And the brigand said, 'But I am a thief and a plunderer.'

And the saint replied, 'I too am a thief and a plunderer.'

And the brigand said, 'But I am a murderer, and the blood of many men cries in my ears.'

And the saint replied, 'I too am a murderer, and in my ears cries the blood of many men.'

And the brigand said, 'I have committed countless crimes.'

And the saint replied, 'I too have committed crimes without number.'

Then the brigand stood up and gazed at the saint, and there was a strange look in his eyes. And when he left us he went skipping down the hill.

And I turned to the saint and said, 'Wherefore did you accuse yourself of uncommitted crimes? See you not that this man went away no longer believing in you?'

And the saint answered, 'It is true he no longer believes in me. But he went away much comforted.'

At that moment we heard the brigand singing in the distance, and the echo of his song filled the valley with gladness.

THE PLUTOCRAT

In my wanderings I once saw upon an island a man-headed, iron-hoofed monster who ate of the earth and drank of the sea incessantly. And for a long while I watched him. Then I approached him and said, 'Have you never enough; is your hunger never satisfied and your thirst never quenched?'

And he answered saying, 'Yes, I am satisfied, nay, I am weary of eating and drinking; but I am afraid that tomorrow there will be no more earth to eat and no more sea to drink.'

THE GREATER SELF

This came to pass. After the coronation of Nufsibaäl King of Byblus, he retired to his bed-chamber – the very room which the three hermit-magicians of the mountain had built for him. He took off his crown and his royal raiment, and stood in the centre of the room thinking of himself, now the all-powerful ruler of Byblus.

Suddenly he turned; and he saw stepping out of the silver mirror which his mother had given him, a naked man.

The king was startled, and he cried out to the man, 'What would you?'

And the naked man answered, 'Naught but this: Why have they crowned you king?'

And the king answered, 'Because I am the noblest man in the land.'

Then the naked man said, 'If you were still more noble, you would not be king.'

And the king said, 'Because I am the mightiest man in the land they crowned me.'

And the naked man said, 'If you were mightier yet, you would not be king.'

Then the king said, 'Because I am the wisest man they crowned me king.'

And the naked man said, 'If you were still wiser you

would not choose to be king.'

Then the king fell to the floor and wept bitterly.

The naked man looked down upon him. Then he took up the crown and with tenderness replaced it upon the king's bent head.

And the naked man, gazing lovingly upon the king, entered into the mirror.

And the king roused, and straightway he looked into the mirror. And he saw there but himself crowned.

WAR AND THE SMALL NATIONS

Once, high above a pasture, where a sheep and a lamb were grazing, an eagle was circling and gazing hungrily down upon the lamb. And as he was about to descend and seize his prey, another eagle appeared and hovered above the sheep and her young with the same hungry intent. Then the two rivals began to fight, filling the sky with their fierce cries.

The sheep looked up and was much astonished. She turned to the lamb and said:

'How strange, my child, that these two noble birds should attack one another. Is not the vast sky large enough for both of them? Pray, my little one, pray in your heart that God may make peace between your winged brothers.'

And the lamb prayed in his heart.

CRITICS

One nightfall a man travelling on horseback towards the sea reached an inn by the roadside. He dismounted and, confident in man and night like all riders towards the sea, he tied his horse to a tree beside the door and entered into the inn.

At midnight, when all were asleep, a thief came and stole the traveller's horse.

In the morning the man awoke, and discovered that his horse was stolen. And he grieved for his horse, and that a man had found it in his heart to steal.

Then his fellow lodgers came and stood around him and began to talk.

And the first man said, 'How foolish of you to tie your horse outside the stable.'

And the second said, 'Still more foolish, without even hobbling the horse!'

And the third man said, 'It is stupid at best to travel to the sea on horseback.'

And the fourth said, 'Only the indolent and the slow of foot own horses.'

Then the traveller was much astonished. At last he cried, 'My friends, because my horse is stolen, you have hastened one and all to tell me my faults and my shortcomings. But strange, not one word of reproach have you uttered about the man who stole my horse.'

POETS

Four poets were sitting around a bowl of punch that stood on a table.

Said the first poet, 'Methinks I see with my third eye the fragrance of this wine hovering in space like a cloud of birds in an enchanted forest.'

The second poet raised his head and said, 'With my inner ear I can hear those mist-birds singing. And the melody holds my heart as the white rose imprisons the bee within her petals.'

The third poet closed his eyes and stretched his arm upwards, and said, 'I touch them with my hand. I feel their wings, like the breath of a sleeping fairy, brushing against my fingers.'

Then the fourth poet rose and lifted up the bowl, and he said, 'Alas, friends! I am too dull of sight and of hearing and of touch. I cannot see the fragrance of this wine, nor hear its song, nor feel the beating of its wings. I perceive but the wine itself. Now therefore must I drink it, that it may sharpen my senses and raise me to your blissful heights.'

And putting the bowl to his lips, he drank the punch to the very last drop.

The three poets, with their mouths open, looked at him aghast, and there was a thirsty yet unlyrical hatred in their eyes.

THE WEATHER-COCK

Said the weather-cock to the wind, 'How tedious and monotonous you are! Can you not blow any other way but in my face? You disturb my God-given stability.'

And the wind did not answer. It only laughed in space.

THE KING OF ARADUS

Once the elders of the city of Aradus presented themselves before the king, and besought of him a decree to forbid to men all wine and all intoxicants within their city.

And the king turned his back upon them and went out from them laughing.

Then the elders departed in dismay.

At the door of the palace they met the lord chamberlain. And the lord chamberlain observed that they were troubled, and he understood their case.

Then he said, 'Pity, my friends! Had you found the king drunk, surely he would have granted you your petition.'

OUT OF MY DEEPER HEART

Out of my deeper heart a bird rose and flew skywards.

Higher and higher did it rise, yet larger and larger did it grow.

At first it was but like a swallow, then a lark, then an eagle, then as vast as a spring cloud, and then it filled the starry heavens.

Out of my heart a bird flew skywards. And it waxed larger as it flew. Yet it left not my heart.

O my faith, my untamed knowledge, how shall I fly to your height and see with you man's larger self pencilled upon the sky?

How shall I turn this sea within me into mist, and move with you in space immeasurable?

How can a prisoner within the temple behold its golden domes?

How shall the heart of a fruit be stretched to envelop the fruit also?

O my faith, I am in chains behind these bars of silver and ebony, and I cannot fly with you.

Yet out of my heart you rise skyward, and it is my heart that holds you, and I shall be content.

DYNASTIES

The queen of Ishana was in travail of childbirth; and the king and the mighty men of his court were waiting in breathless anxiety in the great hall of the Winged Bulls.

At eventide there came suddenly a messenger in haste and prostrated himself before the king, and said, 'I bring glad tidings unto my lord the king, and unto the kingdom and the slaves of the king. Mihrab the Cruel, thy life-long enemy, the king of Bethroun, is dead.'

When the king and the mighty men heard this, they all rose and shouted for joy; for the powerful Mihrab, had he lived longer, had assuredly overcome Ishana and carried the inhabitants captive.

At this moment the court physician also entered the hall of Winged Bulls, and behind him came the royal midwives. And the physician prostrated himself before the king, and said, 'My lord the king shall live for ever, and through countless generations shall he rule over the people of Ishana. For unto thee, O King, is born this very hour a son, who shall be thy heir.'

Then indeed was the soul of the king intoxicated with joy, that in the same moment his foe was dead and the royal line was established.

Now in the city of Ishana lived a true prophet. And the prophet was young, and bold of spirit. And the king that very night ordered that the prophet should be brought before him. And when he was brought, the king said unto him, 'Prophesy now, and foretell what shall be the future of my son who is this day born unto the kingdom.'

And the prophet hesitated not, but said, 'Hearken, O King, and I will indeed prophesy of the future of thy son, that is this day born. The soul of thy enemy, even of thy enemy King Mihrab, who died yester-eve, lingered but a day upon the wind. Then it sought for itself a body to enter into. And that which it entered into was the body of thy son that is born unto thee this hour.'

Then the king was enraged, and with his sword he slew the prophet.

And from that day to this, the wise men of Ishana say one to another secretly, 'Is it not known, and has it not been said from of old, that Ishana is ruled by an enemy?'

KNOWLEDGE AND
HALF-KNOWLEDGE

Four frogs sat upon a log that lay floating on the edge of a river. Suddenly the log was caught by the current and swept slowly down the stream. The frogs were delighted and absorbed, for never before had they sailed.

At length the first frog spoke, and said, 'This is indeed a most marvellous log. It moves as if alive. No such log was ever known before.'

Then the second frog spoke, and said, 'Nay, my friend, the log is like other logs, and does not move. It is the river that is walking to the sea, and carries us and the log with it.'

And the third frog spoke, and said, 'It is neither the log nor the river that moves. The moving is in our thinking. For without thought nothing moves.'

And the three frogs began to wrangle about what was really moving. The quarrel grew hotter and louder, but they could not agree.

Then they turned to the fourth frog, who up to this time had been listening attentively but holding his peace, and they asked his opinion.

And the fourth frog said, 'Each of you is right, and none of you is wrong. The moving is in the log and the water and our thinking also.'

And the three frogs became very angry, for none of

them was willing to admit that his was not the whole truth, and that the other two were not wholly wrong.

Then a strange thing happened. The three frogs got together and pushed the fourth frog off the log into the river.

'SAID A SHEET OF
SNOW-WHITE PAPER . . .'

Said a sheet of snow-white paper, 'Pure was I created, and pure will I remain for ever. I would rather be burnt and turn to white ashes than suffer darkness to touch me or the unclean to come near me.'

The ink-bottle heard what the paper was saying, and it laughed in its dark heart; but it never dared to approach her. And the multicoloured pencils heard her also, and they too never came near her.

And the snow-white sheet of paper did remain pure and chaste for ever, pure and chaste – and empty.

Said the serpent to the lark, 'Thou flyest, yet thou canst not visit the recesses of the earth where the sap of life moveth in perfect silence.'

And the lark answered, 'Aye, thou knowest over much, nay thou art wiser than all things wise – pity thou canst not fly.'

And as if he did not hear, the serpent said, 'Thou canst not see the secrets of the deep, nor move among the treasures of the hidden empire. It was but yesterday I lay in a cave of rubies. It is like the heart of a ripe pomegranate, and the faintest ray of light turns it into a flame-rose. Who but me can behold such marvels?'

And the lark said, 'None, none but thee can lie among the crystal memories of the cycles – pity thou canst not sing.'

And the serpent said, 'I know a plant whose root descends to the bowels of the earth, and he who eats of that root becomes fairer than Ashtarte.'

And the lark said, 'No one, no one but thee could unveil the magic thought of the earth – pity thou canst not fly.'

And the serpent said, 'There is a purple stream that runneth under a mountain, and he who drinketh of it shall become immortal even as the gods. Surely no bird or beast can discover that purple stream.'

And the lark answered, 'If thou willest thou canst become deathless even as the gods – pity thou canst not sing.'

And the serpent said, 'I know a buried temple, which I visit once a moon. It was built by a forgotten race of giants, and upon its walls are graven the secrets of time and space, and he who reads them shall understand that which passeth all understanding.'

And the lark said, 'Verily, if thou so desirest thou canst encircle with thy pliant body all knowledge of time and space – pity thou canst not fly.'

Then the serpent was disgusted, and as he turned and entered into his hole he muttered, 'Empty-headed songster!'

And the lark flew away singing, 'Pity thou canst not sing. Pity, pity, my wise one, thou canst not fly.'

VALUES

Once a man unearthed in his field a marble statue of great beauty. And he took it to a collector who loved all beautiful things and offered it to him for sale, and the collector bought it for a large price. And they parted.

And as the man walked home with his money he thought, and he said to himself, 'How much life this money means! How can anyone give all this for a dead carved stone buried and undreamed of in the earth for a thousand years?'

And now the collector was looking at his statue, and he was thinking, and he said to himself, 'What beauty! What life! The dream of what a soul! – and fresh with the sweet sleep of a thousand years. How can anyone give all this for money, dead and dreamless?'

OTHER SEAS

A fish said to another fish, 'Above this sea of ours there is another sea, with creatures swimming in it – and they live there even as we live here.'

The fish replied, 'Pure fancy! Pure fancy! When you know that everything that leaves our sea by even an inch, and stays out of it, dies. What proof have you of other lives in other seas?'

REPENTANCE

On a moonless night a man entered into his neighbour's garden and stole the largest melon he could find and brought it home.

He opened it and found it still unripe.

Then behold a marvel!

The man's conscience woke and smote him with remorse; and he repented having stolen the melon.

THE DYING MAN AND
THE VULTURE

Wait, wait yet awhile, my eager friend.
I shall yield but too soon this wasted thing,
Whose agony overwrought and useless
Exhausts your patience.
I would not have your honest hunger
Wait upon these moments:
But this chain, though made of breath,
Is hard to break.
And the will to die,
Stronger than all things strong,
Is stayed by a will to live
Feebler than all things feeble.
Forgive me, comrade; I tarry too long.
It is memory that holds my spirit;
A procession of distant days,
A vision of youth spent in a dream,
A face that bids my eyelids not to sleep,
A voice that lingers in my ears,
A hand that touches my hand.
Forgive me that you have waited too long.
It is over now, and all is faded:
The face, the voice, the hand and the mist that brought
    them hither.
The knot is untied.

The cord is cleaved.
And that which is neither food nor drink is withdrawn.
Approach, my hungry comrade;
The board is made ready,
And the fare, frugal and spare,
Is given with love.
Come, and dig your beak here, into the left side,
And tear out of its cage this smaller bird,
Whose wings can beat no more:
I would have it soar with you into the sky.
Come now, my friend, I am your host tonight,
And you my welcome guest.

BEYOND MY SOLITUDE

Beyond my solitude is another solitude, and to him who dwells therein my aloneness is a crowded market-place and my silence a confusion of sounds.

Too young am I and too restless to seek that above-solitude. The voices of yonder valley still hold my ears, and its shadows bar my way and I cannot go.

Beyond these hills is a grove of enchantment and to him who dwells therein my peace is but a whirlwind and my enchantment an illusion.

Too young am I and too riotous to seek that sacred grove. The taste of blood is clinging in my mouth, and the bow and the arrows of my fathers yet linger in my hand and I cannot go.

Beyond this burdened self lives my freer self; and to him my dreams are a battle fought in twilight and my desires the rattling of bones.

Too young am I and too outraged to be my freer self.

And how shall I become my freer self unless I slay my burdened selves, or unless all men become free?

How shall my leaves fly singing upon the wind unless my roots shall wither in the dark?

How shall the eagle in me soar against the sun until my fledglings leave the nest which I with my own beak have built for them?

THE LAST WATCH

At the high tide of night, when the first breath of dawn
came upon the wind, the forerunner, he who calls himself
echo to a voice yet unheard, left his bed-chamber and ascen-
ded to the roof of his house. Long he stood and looked
down upon the slumbering city. Then he raised his head, and
even as if the sleepless spirits of all those asleep had gathered
around him, he opened his lips and spoke, and he said:

'My friends and my neighbours and you who daily pass
my gate, I would speak to you in your sleep, and in the
valley of your dreams I would walk naked and un-
restrained; for heedless are your waking hours and deaf are
your sound-burdened ears.

'Long did I love you and overmuch.

'I love the one among you as though he were all, and all
as if you were one. And in the spring of my heart I sang in
your gardens, and in the summer of my heart I watched at
your threshing-floors.

'Yea, I loved you all, the giant and the pygmy, the leper
and the anointed, and him who gropes in the dark even as
him who dances his days upon the mountains.

'You, the strong, have I loved, though the marks of
your iron hoofs are yet upon my flesh; and you the weak,
though you have drained my faith and wasted my
patience.

'You the rich have I loved, while bitter was your honey to my mouth; and you the poor, though you knew my empty-handed shame.

'You the poet with the bowed lute and blind fingers, you have I loved in self-indulgence; and you the scholar, ever gathering rotted shrouds in potters' fields.

'You the priest I have loved, who sit in the silences of yesterday questioning the fate of my tomorrow; and you the worshippers of gods the images of your own desires.

'You the thirsting woman whose cup is ever full, I have loved in understanding; and you the woman of restless nights, you too I have loved in pity.

'You the talkative have I loved, saying, "Life hath much to say"; and you the dumb have I loved, whispering to myself, "Says he not in silence that which I fain would hear in words?"

'And you the judge and the critic, I have loved also; yet when you have seen me crucified, you said, "He bleeds rhythmically, and the pattern his blood makes upon his white skin is beautiful to behold."

'Yea, I have loved you all, the young and the old, the trembling reed and the oak.

'But, alas, it was the over-abundance of my heart that turned you from me. You would drink love from a cup, but not from a surging river. You would hear love's faint murmur, but when love shouts you would muffle your ears.

'And because I have loved you all you have said, "Too soft and yielding is his heart, and too undiscerning is his path. It is the love of a needy one, who picks crumbs even as he sits at kingly feasts. And it is the love of a weakling, for the strong loves only the strong."

'And because I have loved you overmuch you have said, "It is but the love of a blind man who knows not the beauty of one nor the ugliness of another. And it is the love of the tasteless who drinks vinegar even as wine. And it is the love of the impertinent and the overweening, for what stranger could be our mother and father and sister and brother?"

'This you have said, and more. For often in the market-place you pointed your fingers at me and said mockingly, "There goes the ageless one, the man without seasons, who at the noon hour plays games with our children and at eventide sits with our elders and assumes wisdom and understanding."

'And I said, "I will love them more. Aye, even more. I will hide my love with seeming to hate, and disguise my tenderness as bitterness. I will wear an iron mask, and only when armed and mailed shall I seek them."

'Then I laid a heavy hand upon your bruises, and like a tempest in the night I thundered in your ears.

'From the housetop I proclaimed you hypocrites, Pharisees, tricksters, false and empty earth-bubbles.

'The short-sighted among you I cursed for blind bats, and those too near the earth I likened to soulless moles.

'The eloquent I pronounced fork-tongued, the silent, stone-lipped, and the simple and artless I called the dead never weary of death.

'The seekers after world knowledge I condemned as offenders of the holy spirit and those who would naught but the spirit I branded as hunters of shadows who cast their nets in flat waters and catch but their own images.

'Thus with my lips have I denounced you, while my heart, bleeding within me, called you tender names.

'It was love lashed by its own self that spoke. It was pride half slain that fluttered in the dust. It was my hunger for your love that raged from the housetop, while my own love, kneeling in silence, prayed your forgiveness.

'But behold a miracle!

'It was my disguise that opened your eyes, and my seeming to hate that woke your hearts.

'And now you love me.

'You love the swords that strike you and the arrows that crave your breast. For it comforts you to be wounded and only when you drink of your own blood can you be intoxicated.

'Like moths that seek destruction in the flame you gather daily in my garden; and with faces uplifted and eyes enchanted you watch me tear the fabric of your days. And in whispers you say the one to the other, "He sees with the light of God. He speaks like the prophets of old. He unveils our souls and unlocks our hearts, and like the eagle that knows the way of foxes he knows our ways."

'Aye, in truth, I know your ways, but only as an eagle knows the ways of his fledglings. And I fain would disclose my secret. Yet in my need for your nearness I feign remoteness, and in fear of the ebb tide of your love I guard the floodgates of my love.'

After saying these things the forerunner covered his face with his hands and wept bitterly. For he knew in his heart that love humiliated in its nakedness is greater than love that seeks triumph in disguise; and he was ashamed.

But suddenly he raised his head, and like one waking from sleep he outstretched his arms and said, 'Night is over, and we children of night must die when dawn comes

43

leaping upon the hills; and out of our ashes a mightier love shall rise. And it shall laugh in the sun, and it shall be deathless.'

PART TWO

Complete Short Pieces

He who listens to truth is not less
than he who utters truth.

Sand and Foam, 65

THE CREATION

The god separated a spirit from himself and fashioned it into beauty. He showered upon her all the blessings of gracefulness and kindness. He gave her the cup of happiness and said, 'Drink not from this cup unless you forget the past and the future, for happiness is naught but the moment.' And he also gave her a cup of sorrow and said, 'Drink from this cup and you will understand the meaning of the fleeting instants of the joy of life, for sorrow ever abounds.'

And the god bestowed upon her a love that would desert her for ever upon her first sigh of earthly satisfaction, and a sweetness that would vanish with her first awareness of flattery.

And he gave her wisdom from heaven to lead her to the all-righteous path, and placed in the depth of her heart an eye that sees the unseen, and created in her an affection and goodness towards all things. He dressed her with raiment of hopes spun by the angels of heaven from the sinews of the rainbow. And he cloaked her in the shadow of confusion, which is the dawn of life and light.

Then the god took consuming fire from the furnace of anger, and searing wind from the desert of ignorance, and sharp-cutting sands from the shore of selfishness, and coarse earth from under the feet of ages, and combined them all and fashioned man. He gave to man a blind power that rages and drives him into a madness which extinguishes only before gratification of desire, and placed life in him which is the spectre of death.

And the god laughed and cried. He felt an overwhelming love and pity for man, and sheltered him beneath his guidance.   *1 T*, 61–2

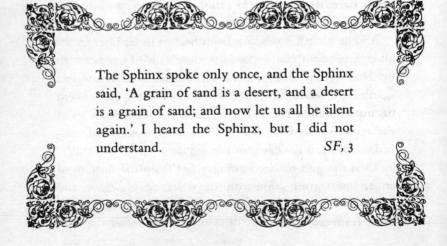

The Sphinx spoke only once, and the Sphinx said, 'A grain of sand is a desert, and a desert is a grain of sand; and now let us all be silent again.' I heard the Sphinx, but I did not understand.   *SF,* 3

THE GREATER SEA

My soul and I went to the great sea to bathe. And when we reached the shore, we went about looking for a hidden and lonely place.

But as we walked, we saw a man sitting on a grey rock taking pinches of salt from a bag and throwing them into the sea.

'This is the pessimist,' said my soul. 'Let us leave this place. We cannot bathe here.'

We walked on until we reached an inlet. There we saw, standing on a white rock, a man holding a bejewelled box, from which he took sugar and threw it into the sea.

'And this is the optimist,' said my soul. 'And he too must not see our naked bodies.'

Further on we walked. And on a beach we saw a man picking up dead fish and tenderly putting them back into the water.

'And we cannot bathe before him,' said my soul. 'He is the humane philanthropist.'

And we passed on.

Then we came where we saw a man tracing his shadow on the sand. Great waves came and erased it. But he went on tracing it again and again.

'He is the mystic,' said my soul. 'Let us leave him.'

And we walked on, till in a quiet cave we saw a man

scooping up the foam and putting it into an alabaster bowl.

'He is the idealist,' said my soul. 'Surely he must not see our nudity.'

And on we walked. Suddenly we heard a voice crying, 'This is the sea. This is the deep sea. This is the vast and mighty sea.' And when we reached the voice it was a man whose back was turned to the sea, and at his ear he held a shell, listening to its murmur.

And my soul said, 'Let us pass on. He is the realist, who turns his back on the whole he cannot grasp, and busies himself with a fragment.'

So we passed on. And in a weedy place among the rocks was a man with his head buried in the sand. And I said to my soul, 'We can bathe here, for he cannot see us.'

'Nay,' said my soul, 'for he is the most deadly of them all. He is the puritan.'

Then a great sadness came over the face of my soul, and into her voice.

'Let us go from here,' she said. 'For there is no lonely, hidden place where we can bathe. I would not have this wind lift my golden hair, or bare my white bosom in this air, or let the light disclose my sacred nakedness.'

Then we left that sea to seek the Greater Sea.   *M*, 55–8

REVELATION

When the night waxed deep and slumber cast its cloak
  upon the face of the earth,
I left my bed and sought the sea, saying to myself:
'The sea never sleeps, and the wakefulness of the sea brings
  comfort to a sleepless soul.'
When I reached the shore, the mist had already descended
  from the mountain tops
And covered the world as a veil adorns the face of a
  maiden.

There I stood gazing at the waves, listening to their singing,
  and considering the power that lies behind them –
The power that travels with the storm, and rages with the
  volcano, that smiles with smiling flowers and makes
  melody with murmuring brooks.

After a while I turned, and lo,
I beheld three figures sitting upon a rock nearby,
And I saw that the mist veiled them, and yet it veiled them
  not.

Slowly I walked towards the rock whereon they sat,
  drawn by some power which I know not.
A few paces off I stood and gazed upon them, for there
  was magic in the place

Which crystallized my purpose and bestirred my fancy.

And at that moment one of the three arose, and with a voice that seemed to come from the sea depths he said:

'Life without love is like a tree without blossoms or fruit.

And love without beauty is like flowers without fragrance, and fruit without seeds.

Life, Love, and Beauty are three entities in one self, free and boundless,

Which know neither change nor separation.'

This he said, and sat again in his place.

Then the second figure arose, and with a voice like the roar of rushing waters he said:

'Life without rebellion is like the seasons without a spring.

And rebellion without right is like spring in an arid and barren desert.

Life, Rebellion, and Right are three entities in one self,

And in them is neither change nor separation.'

This he said, and sat again in his place.

Then the third figure arose, and spoke with a voice like the peal of the thunder, saying:

'Life without freedom is like a body without a spirit.

And freedom without thought is like a spirit confounded.

Life, Freedom, and Thought are three entities in one eternal self,

Which neither vanish nor pass away.'

Then the three arose and with voices of majesty and awe they spoke:

'Love and all that it begets,

Rebellion and all that it creates,

Freedom and all that it generates,

These three are aspects of God . . .
And God is the infinite mind of the finite and conscious
world.'

Then silence followed, filled with the stirring of invisible
wings and the tremor of the ethereal bodies.
And I closed my eyes, listening to the echo of the saying
which I heard.

When I opened my eyes, I beheld naught but the sea
hidden beneath a blanket of mist;
And I moved closer towards that rock
And I beheld naught but a pillar of incense rising unto the
sky.   *PP,* 12–15

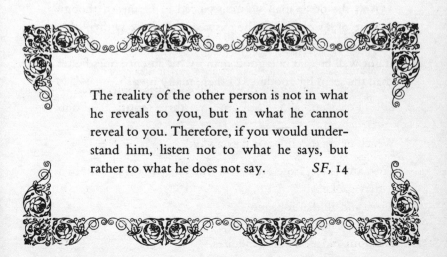

The reality of the other person is not in what
he reveals to you, but in what he cannot
reveal to you. Therefore, if you would understand him, listen not to what he says, but
rather to what he does not say.   *SF,* 14

FINDING GOD

Two men were walking in the valley, and one man pointed with his finger towards the mountain side, and said, 'See you that hermitage? There lives a man who has long divorced the world. He seeks but after God, and naught else upon this earth.'

And the other man said, 'He shall not find God until he leaves his hermitage, and the aloneness of his hermitage, and returns to our world, to share our joy and pain, to dance with our dancers at the wedding feast, and to weep with those who weep around the coffins of our dead.'

And the other man was convinced in his heart, though in spite of his conviction he answered, 'I agree with all that you say, yet I believe the hermit is a good man. And may it not well be that one good man by his absence does better than the seeming goodness of these many men?' *W*, 87

THE PATH

There lived among the hills a woman and her son, and he was her first-born and her only child.

And the boy died of a fever whilst the physician stood by.

The mother was distraught with sorrow, and she cried to the physician and besought him saying, 'Tell me, tell me, what was it that made quiet his striving and silent his song?'

And the physician said, 'It was the fever.'

And the mother said, 'What is the fever?'

And the physician answered, 'I cannot explain it. It is a thing infinitely small that visits the body, and we cannot see it with our human eye.'

Then the physician left her. And she kept repeating to herself, 'Something infinitely small. We cannot see it with our human eye.'

And at evening the priest came to console her. And she wept and she cried out saying, 'Oh, why have I lost my son, my only son, my first-born?'

And the priest answered, 'My child, it is the will of God.'

And the woman said, 'What is God and where is God? I would see God that I may tear my bosom before Him, and pour the blood of my heart at His feet. Tell me where I shall find Him.'

And the priest said, 'God is infinitely vast. He is not to be seen with the human eye.'

Then the woman cried out, 'The infinitely small has slain my son through the will of the infinitely great! Then what are we? What are we?'

At that moment the woman's mother came into the room with the shroud for the dead boy, and she heard the words of the priest and also her daughter's cry. And she laid down the shroud, and took her daughter's hand in her own hand, and she said, 'My daughter, we ourselves are the infinitely small and the infinitely great; and we are the path between the two.'   *W*, 80–81

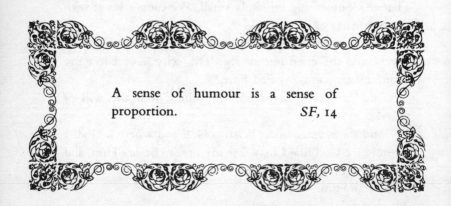

A sense of humour is a sense of proportion.   *SF*, 14

THE ASTRONOMER

In the shadow of the temple my friend and I saw a blind man sitting alone. And my friend said, 'Behold the wisest man of our land.'

Then I left my friend and approached the blind man and greeted him. And we conversed.

After a while I said, 'Forgive my question, but since when hast thou been blind?'

'From my birth,' he answered.

Said I, 'And what path of wisdom followest thou?'

Said he, 'I am an astronomer.'

Then he placed his hand upon his breast, saying, 'I watch all these suns and moons and stars.'   *M*, 61

THE QUEST

A thousand years ago two philosophers met on a slope of Lebanon, and one said to the other, 'Where goest thou?'

And the other answered, 'I am seeking after the fountain of youth which I know wells out among these hills. I have found writings which tell of that fountain flowering towards the sun. And you, what are you seeking?'

The first man answered, 'I am seeking after the mystery of death.'

Then each of the two philosophers conceived that the other was lacking in his great science, and they began to wrangle, and to accuse each other of spiritual blindness.

Now while the two philosophers were loud upon the wind, a stranger, a man who was deemed a simpleton in his own village, passed by, and when he heard the two in hot dispute, he stood awhile and listened to their argument.

Then he came near to them and said, 'My good men, it seems that you both really belong to the same school of philosophy, and that you are speaking of the same thing, only you speak in different words. One of you seeks the fountain of youth, and the other seeks the mystery of death. Yet indeed they are but one, and as one they dwell in you both.'

Then the stranger turned away saying, 'Farewell, sages.'

And as he departed he laughed a patient laughter.

The two philosophers looked at each other in silence for a moment, and then they laughed also. And one of them said, 'Well now, shall we not walk and seek together?'   *W*, 77–8

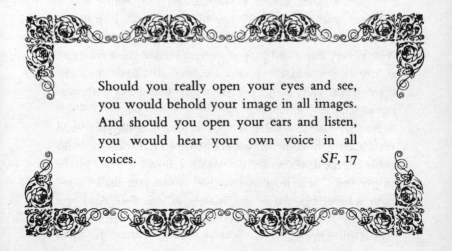

Should you really open your eyes and see, you would behold your image in all images. And should you open your ears and listen, you would hear your own voice in all voices.   *SF*, 17

THE RIVER

In the valley of Kadisha where the mighty river flows, two little streams met and spoke to one another.

One stream said, 'How came you, my friend, and how was your path?'

And the other answered, 'My path was most encumbered. The wheel of the mill was broken, and the master farmer, who used to conduct me from my channel to his plants, is dead. I struggled down oozing with the filth of those who do naught but sit and bake their laziness in the sun. But how was your path, my brother?'

And the other stream answered and said, 'Mine was a different path. I came down the hills among fragrant flowers and shy willows; men and women drank of me with silvery cups, and little children paddled their rosy feet at my edges, and there was laughter all about me, and there were sweet songs. What a pity that your path was not so happy.'

At that moment the river spoke with a loud voice and said, 'Come in, come in, we are going to the sea. Come in, come in, speak no more. Be with me now. We are going to the sea. Come in, come in, for in me you shall forget your wanderings, sad or gay. Come in, come in. And you and I will forget all our ways when we reach the heart of our mother the sea.'   *W*, 88–9

THE FIELD OF ZAAD

Upon the road of Zaad a traveller met a man who lived in a nearby village, and the traveller, pointing with his hand to a vast field, asked the man, saying, 'Was not this the battleground where King Ahlam overcame his enemies?'

And the man answered and said, 'This has never been a battleground. There once stood on this field the great city of Zaad, and it was burnt down to ashes. But now it is a good field, is it not?'

And the traveller and the man parted.

Not half a mile further the traveller met another man, and pointing to the field again, he said, 'So that is where the great city of Zaad once stood?'

And the man said, 'There has never been a city in this place. But once there was a monastery here, and it was destroyed by the people of the South Country.'

Shortly after, on that very road of Zaad, the traveller met a third man, and pointing once more to the vast field he said, 'Is it not true that this is the place where once there stood a great monastery?'

But the man answered, 'There has never been a monastery in this neighbourhood, but our fathers and our forefathers have told us that once there fell a great meteor on this field.'

Then the traveller walked on, wondering in his heart.

And he met a very old man, and saluting him he said, 'Sir, upon this road I have met three men who live in the neighbourhood and I have asked each of them about this field, and each one denied what the other had said, and each one told me a new tale that the other had not told.'

Then the old man raised his head and answered, 'My friend, each every one of these men told you what was indeed so; but few of us are able to add fact to different fact and make a truth thereof.'   *W*, 54–5

Genius is but a robin's song at the beginning of a slow spring.   *SF*, 25

PERFECTION

You ask me, my brother, when will man reach perfection.
  Hear my answer:
Man approaches perfection when he feels that he is an
  infinite space and a sea without a shore,
An everlasting fire, an unquenchable light,
A calm wind or a raging tempest, a thundering sky or a
  rainy heaven,
A singing brook or a wailing rivulet, a tree abloom in
  Spring, or a naked sapling
In Autumn,
A rising mountain or a descending valley,
A fertile plain or a desert.

When man feels all these, he has already reached halfway
  to perfection. To attain his goal he must then perceive
  that he is a child dependent upon his mother, a father
  responsible for his family,
A youth lost in love,
An ancient wrestling against his past,
A worshipper in his temple, a criminal in his prison,
A scholar amidst his parchments,
An ignorant soul stumbling between the darkness of his
  night and the obscurity of his day,
A nun suffering between the flowers of her faith and the
  thistles of her loneliness,

A prostitute caught between the fangs of her weakness and the claws of her needs,

A poor man trapped between his bitterness and his submission,

A rich man between his greed and his conscience,

A poet between the mist of his twilight and the rays of his dawn.

Who can experience, see, and understand these things can reach perfection and become a shadow of God's Shadow. *TM*, 113–14

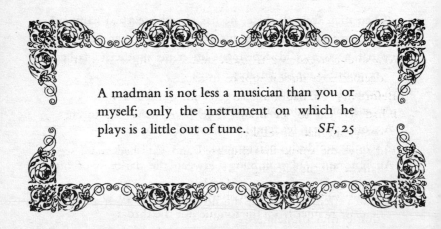

A madman is not less a musician than you or myself; only the instrument on which he plays is a little out of tune. *SF*, 25

MY SOUL COUNSELLED ME

My soul spoke unto me and counselled me to love all that
others hate,
And to befriend those whom others defame.
My soul counselled me and revealed unto me that love
dignifies not alone the one who loves, but also the
beloved.
Unto that day love was for me a thread of cobweb
between two flowers, close to one another;
But now it has become a halo with neither beginning nor
end,
Encircling all that has been, and waxing eternally to embrace all that shall be.

My soul counselled me and taught me to see beauty veiled
by form and colour.
My soul charged me to gaze steadfastly upon all that is
deemed ugly until it appears lovely.
Before my soul had thus charged and counselled me,
I had seemed to see beauty like unto wavering torches
between pillars of smoke;
But now the smoke has dispersed and vanished and I see
naught but the burning.

My soul counselled me and charged me to listen for voices
that rise neither from the tongue nor the throat.

Before that day I heard but dully, and naught save clamour
and loud cries came to my ears;
But now I have learned to listen to silence,
To hear its choirs singing the songs of ages,
Chanting the hymns of space, and disclosing the secrets of
eternity.

My soul spoke unto me and counselled me to quench my
thirst with that wine which may not be poured into
cups,
Nor lifted by hands, nor touched by lips.
Unto that day my thirst was like a dim spark laid in ashes
To be put out by a draught from any spring;
But now my strong yearning has become my cup,
Love has become my wine, and loneliness my joy.

My soul counselled me and charged me to seek that which
is unseen;
And my soul revealed unto me that the thing we grasp is
the thing we desire.
In other days I was content with warmth in winter, and
with a cooling zephyr in the summer season;
But now my fingers are become as mist,
Letting fall all that they have held, to mingle with the
unseen that I now desire.

My soul spoke to me and invited me to breathe the
fragrance from a plant
That has neither root nor stalk nor blossom, and that no
eye has seen.
Before my soul counselled me thus, I sought perfumes in
the gardens,
In jars of sweet-smelling herbs and vessels of incense;

But now I am aware only of an incense that may not be
   burned,
I breathe an air more fragrant than all earth's gardens and
   all the winds of space.

My soul counselled me and charged me to answer and say
   'I follow', when the unknown and the adventurous call
   unto me.
Hitherto I had answered naught but the voice of the crier
   in the market-place,
Nor did I pursue aught save roads charted and well
   trodden;
But now the known has become a steed that I mount to
   seek the unknown,
And the road has become a ladder by which I may climb
   to the perilous summit.

My soul counselled me and admonished me to measure
   time with this saying:
'There was a yesterday and there shall be a tomorrow.'
Unto that hour I deemed the past an epoch that is lost and
   shall be forgotten,
And the future I deemed an era that I may not attain;
But now I have learned this:
That in the brief present all time, with all that is in time,
Is achieved and come true.

My soul spoke and revealed unto me that I am not bound
   in space by the words:
'Here, there, and over there.'
Hitherto I stood upon my hill, and every other hill seemed
   distant and far away;
But now I know that the hill whereon I dwell is indeed all
   hills,

And the valley whereunto I descend comprehends all valleys.

My soul counselled me and besought me to watch while others sleep
And to seek my pillow while they are wakeful,
For in all my years I had not perceived their dreams, nor they mine.
But now I am winged by day in my dreaming,
And when they sleep I behold them free upon the night,
And I rejoice in their freedom.

My soul counselled me and charged me lest I be exalted because of overpraise
And lest I be distressed for fear of blame.
Until that day I doubted the worth of my own handiwork;
But now I have learned this:
That the trees blossom in spring, and bear fruit in summer,
And drop their leaves in autumn to become utterly naked in winter
Without exaltation and without fear or shame.

My soul counselled me and assured me
That I am neither higher than the pygmy nor lower than the giant.
Before that day I beheld mankind as two men,
The one a weakling whom I derided or pitied,
And the other a mighty man whom I would either follow, or oppose in rebellion.
But now I know that I was formed even from the same dust of which all men are created,

That my elements are their elements, and my inner self is
their inner self.
My struggle is their struggle, and their pilgrimage is mine
own.
If they transgress, I am also the transgressor,
And if they do well, then I have a share in their well-
doing.
If they arise, I too arise with them; if they stay behind, I
also, to company them.

My soul counselled me and instructed me to see that the
light which I carry is not my light,
That my song was not created within me;
For though I travel with the light, I am not the light,
And though I am a lute fastened with strings,
I am not the lute-player.

My soul counselled me, my brother, and enlightened me.
And oftentimes has your soul counselled and enlightened
you.
For you are like me, and there is no difference between us
Save that I speak of what is within me in words that I have
heard in my silence,
And you guard what is within you, and your guardianship
is as goodly as my much speaking.   *PP*, 21–8

SONG OF MAN

I was here from the moment of the
Beginning, and here I am still. And
I shall remain here until the end
Of the world, for there is no
Ending to my grief-stricken being.

I roamed the infinite sky, and
Soared in the ideal world, and
Floated through the firmament. But
Here I am, prisoner of measurement.

I heard the teachings of Confucius;
I listened to Brahma's wisdom;
I sat by Buddha under the Tree of Knowledge.
Yet here am I, existing with ignorance
And heresy.

I was on Sinai when Jehovah approached Moses;
I saw the Nazarene's miracles at the Jordan;
I was in Medina when Mohammed visited.
Yet here I am, prisoner of bewilderment.

Then I witnessed the might of Babylon;
I learned of the glory of Egypt;
I viewed the warring greatness of Rome.
Yet my earlier teachings showed the

Weakness and sorrow of those achievements.

I conversed with the magicians of Ain Dour;
I debated with the priests of Assyria;
I gleaned depth from the prophets of Palestine.
Yet I am still seeking the truth.

I gathered wisdom from quiet India;
I probed the antiquity of Arabia;
I heard all that can be heard.
Yet my heart is deaf and blind.

I suffered at the hands of despotic rulers;
I suffered slavery under insane invaders;
I suffered hunger imposed by tyranny;
Yet I still possess some inner power
With which I struggle to greet each day.

My mind is filled, but my heart is empty;
My body is old, but my heart is an infant.
Perhaps in youth my heart will grow, but I
Pray to grow old and reach the moment of
My return to God. Only then will my heart fill!

I was here from the moment of the
Beginning, and here I am still. And
I shall remain here until the end
Of the world, for there is no
Ending to my grief-stricken being.

1 T, 239–40

SATAN

The people looked upon Father Samaan as their guide in the field of spiritual and theological matters, for he was an authority and a source of deep information on venial and mortal sins, well versed in the secrets of paradise, hell, and purgatory.

Father Samaan's mission in North Lebanon was to travel from one village to another, preaching and curing the people from the spiritual disease of sin, and saving them from the horrible trap of Satan. The Reverend Father waged constant war with Satan. The fellahin honoured and respected this clergyman, and were always anxious to buy his advice or prayers with pieces of gold and silver; and at every harvest they would present him with the finest fruits of their fields.

One evening in autumn, as Father Samaan walked his way towards a solitary village, crossing those valleys and hills, he heard a painful cry emerging from a ditch at the side of the road. He stopped and looked in the direction of the voice, and saw an unclothed man lying on the ground. Streams of blood oozed from deep wounds in his head and chest. He was moaning pitifully for aid, saying, 'Save me, help me. Have mercy on me, I am dying.' Father Samaan looked with perplexity at the sufferer, and said within himself, 'This man must be a thief. He probably tried to rob the wayfarers and failed. Someone has wounded him, and I fear that should he die I may be accused of having taken his life.'

Having thus pondered the situation, he resumed his journey, whereupon the dying man stopped him, calling out, 'Do not leave me! I am dying!' Then the Father meditated again, and his face became pale as he realized he was refusing to help. His lips quivered, but he spoke to himself, saying, 'He must surely be one of the madmen wandering in the wilderness. The sight of his wounds brings fear into my heart; what shall I do? Surely a spiritual doctor is not capable of treating flesh-wounded bodies.' Father Samaan walked ahead a few paces when the near-corpse uttered a painful plaint that melted the heart of the rock and he gasped, 'Come close to me! Come, for we have been friends a long time. You are Father Samaan, the good shepherd, and I am not a thief nor a madman. Come close, and do not let me die in this deserted place. Come, and I will tell you who I am.'

Father Samaan came close to the man, knelt, and stared at him; but he saw a strange face with contrasting features; he saw intelligence with slyness, ugliness with beauty, and wickedness with softness. He withdrew to his feet sharply, and exclaimed, 'Who are you?'

With a fainting voice, the dying man said, 'Fear me not, Father, for we have been strong friends for long. Help me to stand, and take me to the nearby streamlet and cleanse my wounds with your linens.' And the Father inquired, 'Tell me who you are, for I do not know you, nor even remember having seen you.'

And the man replied with an agonizing voice, 'You know my identity! You have seen me one thousand times and you speak of me each day. I am dearer to you than your own life.' And the Father reprimanded, 'You are a lying imposter! A dying man should tell the truth. I have never seen your evil face in my entire life. Tell me who you are, or I will suffer you to die, soaked in your own escaping life.' And the wounded man moved slowly and looked into the clergyman's eyes, and upon his lips appeared a mystic smile; and in a quiet, deep and smooth voice he said, 'I am Satan.'

Upon hearing the fearful word, Father Samaan uttered a terrible cry that shook the far corners of the valley; then he stared, and realized that the dying man's body, with its grotesque distortions, coincided with the likeness of Satan in a religious picture hanging on the wall of the village church. He trembled and cried out, saying, 'God has shown me your hellish image and justly caused me to hate you; cursed be you for evermore! The mangled lamb must be destroyed by the shepherd lest he will infect the other lambs!'

Satan answered, 'Be not in haste, Father, and lose not this fleeting time in empty talk. Come and close my wounds quickly, before life departs from my body.' And the clergyman retorted, 'The hands which offer a daily sacrifice to God shall not touch a body made of the secretion of hell. You must die accursed by the tongues of the ages, and the lips of humanity, for you are the enemy of humanity, and it is your avowed purpose to destroy all virtue.'

Satan moved in anguish, raising himself upon one elbow, and responded, 'You know not what you are saying, nor understand the crime you are committing upon yourself. Give heed, for I will relate my story. Today I walked alone in this solitary valley. When I reached this place, a group of angels descended to attack, and struck me severely; had it not been for one of them, who carried a blazing sword with two sharp edges, I would have driven them off, but I had no power against the brilliant sword.' And Satan ceased talking for a moment, as he pressed a shaking hand upon a deep wound in his side. Then he continued, 'The armed angel — I believe he was Michael — was an expert gladiator. Had I not thrown myself to the friendly ground and feigned to have been slain, he would have torn me into brutal death.'

With voice of triumph, and casting his eyes heavenwards, the Father offered, 'Blessed be Michael's name, who has saved humanity from this vicious enemy.'

And Satan protested, 'My disdain for humanity is not greater than your hatred for yourself. You are blessing Michael, who never has come to your rescue. You are cursing me in the hour of my defeat, even though I was, and still am, the source of your tranquillity and happiness. You deny me your blessing, and extend not your kindness, but you live and prosper in the shadow of my being. You have adopted my existence as an excuse and weapon for your career, and you employ my name in justification for your deeds. Has not my past caused you to be in need of my present and future? Have you reached your goal in amassing the required wealth? Have you found it impossible to extract more gold and silver from your followers, using my kingdom as a threat?

'Do you not realize that you will starve to death if I were to die? What would you do tomorrow if you allowed me to die today? What vocation would you pursue if my name disappeared? For decades you have been roaming these villages and warning the people against falling into my hands. They have bought your advice with their poor dinars and with the products of their land. What would they buy from you tomorrow, if they discovered that their wicked enemy no longer existed? Your occupation would die with me, for the people would be safe from sin. As a clergyman, do you not realize that Satan's existence alone has created his enemy, the Church? That ancient conflict is the secret hand which removes the gold and silver from the faithful's pocket and deposits it forever into the pouch of the preacher and missionary. How can you permit me to die here, when you know it will surely cause you to lose your prestige, your church, your home, and your livelihood?'

Satan became silent for a moment and his humility was now converted into a confident independence, and he continued, 'Father, you are proud, but ignorant. I will disclose to you the history of belief, and in it you will find the truth which joins both of our beings, and ties my existence with your very conscience.

'In the first hour of the beginning of time, man stood before the face of the sun and stretched forth his arms and cried for the first time, saying, "Behind the sky there is a great and loving and benevolent God." The man turned his back to the great circle of light and saw his shadow upon the earth, and he hailed, "In the depths of the earth there is a dark devil who loves wickedness."

'And the man walked towards his cave, whispering to himself, "I am between two compelling forces, one in whom I must take refuge, and the other against whom I must struggle." And the ages marched in procession while man existed between two powers, one that he blessed because it exalted him, and one that he cursed because it frightened him. But he never perceived the meaning of a blessing or of a curse; he was between the two, like a tree between summer, when it blooms, and winter, when it shivers.

'When man saw the dawn of civilization, which is human understanding, the family as a unit came into being. Then came the tribes, whereupon labour was divided according to ability and inclination; one clan cultivated the land, another built shelters, others wove raiment or hunted food. Subsequently divination made its appearance upon the earth, and this was the first career adopted by man which possessed no essential urge or necessity.'

Satan ceased talking for a moment. Then he laughed and his mirth shook the empty valley, but his laughter reminded him of his wounds, and he placed his hand on his side, suffering with pain. He steadied himself and continued, 'Divination appeared and grew on earth in strange fashion.

'There was a man in the first tribe called La Wiss. I know not the origin of his name. He was an intelligent creature, but extremely indolent and he detested work in the cultivation of land, construction of shelters, grazing of cattle or any pursuit requiring bodily movement or exertion. And since food, during that era, could not be obtained except by arduous toil, La Wiss slept many nights with an empty stomach.

'One summer night, as the members of that clan were gathered around the hut of their chief, talking of the outcome of their day and waiting for their slumber time, a man suddenly leaped to his feet, pointed towards the moon, and cried out, saying, "Look at the night god! His face is dark, and his beauty has vanished, and he has turned into a black stone hanging in the dome of the sky!" The multitude gazed at the moon, shouted in awe, and shook with fear, as if the hands of darkness had clutched their hearts, for they saw the night god slowly turning into a dark ball which changed the bright countenance of the earth and caused the hills and valleys before their eyes to disappear behind a black veil.

'At that moment, La Wiss, who had seen an eclipse before, and understood its simple cause, stepped forward to make much of this opportunity. He stood in the midst of the throng, lifted his hands to the sky, and in a strong voice he addressed them, saying, "Kneel and pray, for the evil god of obscurity is locked in struggle with the illuminating night god; if the evil god conquers him, we will all perish, but if the night god triumphs over him, we will remain alive. Pray now and worship. Cover your faces with earth. Close your eyes, and lift not your heads towards the sky, for he who witnesses the two gods wrestling will lose his sight and mind, and will remain blind and insane all his life! Bend your heads low, and with all your hearts urge the night god against his enemy, who is our mortal enemy!"

'Thus did La Wiss continue talking, using many cryptic words of his own fabrication which they had never heard. After this crafty deception, as the moon returned to its previous glory, La Wiss raised his voice louder than before and said impressively, "Rise now, and look at the night god who has triumphed over his evil enemy. He is resuming his journey among the stars. Let it be known that through your prayers you have helped him to overcome the devil of darkness. He is well pleased now, and brighter than ever."

'The multitude rose and gazed at the moon that was shining in full beam. Their fear became tranquillity, and their confusion was now joy. They commenced dancing and singing and striking with their thick sticks upon sheets of iron, filling the valleys with their clamour and shouting.

'That night, the chief of the tribe called La Wiss and spoke to him, saying, "You have done something that no man has ever done. You have demonstrated knowledge of a hidden secret that no other among us understands. Reflecting the will of my people, you are to be the highest ranking member, after me, in the tribe. I am the strongest man, and you are the wisest and most learned person. You are the medium between our people and the gods, whose desires and deeds you are to interpret, and you will teach us those things necessary to gain their blessings and love."

'And La Wiss slyly assured, "Everything the human god reveals to me in my divine dreams will be conveyed to you in awakeness, and you may be confident that I will act directly between you and him." The chief was assured, and gave La Wiss two horses, seven calves, seventy sheep and seventy lambs; and he spoke to him, saying, "The men of the tribe shall build for you a strong house, and we will give you at the end of each harvest season a part of the crop of the land so you may live as an honourable and respected master."

'La Wiss rose and started to leave, but the chief stopped him, saying, "Who and what is the one whom you call the human god? Who is this daring god who wrestles with the glorious night god? We have never pondered him before." La Wiss rubbed his forehead and answered him, saying, "My honourable master, in the olden time, before the creation of man, all the gods were living peacefully together in an upper world behind the vastness of the stars. The god of gods was their father, and knew what they did not know, and did what they were unable to do. He kept for himself the divine secrets that existed beyond the eternal laws. During the seventh epoch of the twelfth age, the spirit of Bahtaar, who hated the great god, revolted and stood before his father, and said, 'Why do you keep for yourself the power of great authority upon all creatures, hiding away from us the secrets and laws of the universe? Are we not your children who believe in you and share with you the great understanding and the perpetual being?'

"The god of gods became enraged and said, 'I shall preserve for myself the primary power and the great authority and the essential secrets, for I am the beginning and the end.'

"And Bahtaar answered him saying, 'Unless you share with me your might and power, I and my children and my children's children will revolt against you!' At that moment, the god of gods stood upon his throne in the deep heavens, and drew forth a sword, and grasped the sun as a shield; and with a voice that shook all corners of eternity he shouted out, saying, 'Descend, you evil rebel, to the dismal lower world where darkness and misery exist! There you shall remain in exile, wandering until the sun turns into ashes and the stars into dispersed particles!' In that hour, Bahtaar descended from the upper world into the lower world, where all the evil spirits dwelt. Thereupon, he swore by the secret of life that he would fight his father and brothers by trapping every soul who loved them."

'As the chief listened, his forehead wrinkled and his face

turned pale. He ventured, "Then the name of the evil god is Bahtaar?" and La Wiss responded, "His name was Bahtaar when he was in the upper world, but when he entered into the lower world, he adopted successively the names Baalzaboul, Satanail, Balial, Zamiel, Ahriman, Mara, Abdon, Devil, and finally Satan, which is the most famous."

'The chief repeated the word "Satan" many times with a quivering voice that sounded like the rustling of the dry branches at the passing of the wind; then he asked, "Why does Satan hate man as much as he hates the gods?"

'And La Wiss responded quickly, "He hates man because man is a descendant of Satan's brothers and sisters." The chief exclaimed, "Then Satan is the cousin of man!" In a voice mingled with confusion and annoyance, he retorted, "Yes, master, but he is their great enemy who fills their days with misery and their nights with horrible dreams. He is the power who directs the tempest towards their hovels, and brings famine upon their plantation, and disease upon them and their animals. He is an evil and powerful god; he is wicked, and he rejoices when we are in sorrow, and he mourns when we are joyous. We must, through my knowledge, examine him thoroughly, in order to avoid his evil; we must study his character, so we will not step upon his trap-laden path."

'The chief leaned his head upon his thick stick and whispered, saying, "I have learned now the inner secret of that strange power who directs the tempest towards our homes and brings the pestilence upon us and our cattle. The people shall learn all that I have comprehended now, and La Wiss will be blessed, honoured and glorified for revealing to them the mystery of their powerful enemy, and directing them away from the road of evil."

'And La Wiss left the chief of the tribe and went to his retiring place, happy over his ingenuity, and intoxicated with the wine of his pleasure and fancy. For the first time, the chief and all the tribe, except La Wiss, spent the night slumbering in beds surrounded by horrible ghosts, fearful spectres, and disturbing dreams.'

Satan ceased talking for a moment, while Father Samaan stared at him as one bewildered, and upon the Father's lips appeared the sickly laughter of death. Then Satan continued, 'Thus divination came to this earth, and thus was my existence the cause for its appearance. La Wiss was the first who adopted my cruelty as a vocation. After the death of La Wiss, this occupation circulated through his children and prospered until it became a perfect and divine profession, pursued by those whose minds are ripe with knowledge, and whose souls are noble, and whose hearts are pure, and whose fancy is vast.

'In Babylon, the people bowed seven times in worshipping before a priest who fought me with his chantings. In Nineveh, they looked upon a man, who claimed to have known my inner secrets, as a golden link between God and man. In Tibet, they called the person who wrestled with me the son of the sun and moon. In Byblus, Ephesus and Antioch, they offered their children's lives in sacrifice to my opponents. In Jerusalem and Rome, they placed their lives in the hands of those who claimed they hated me and fought me with all their might.

'In every city under the sun my name was the axis of the educational circle of religion, arts, and philosophy. Had it not been for me, no temples would have been built, no towers or palaces would have been erected. I am the courage that creates resolution in man. I am the source that provokes originality of thought. I am the hand that moves man's hands. I am Satan everlasting. I am Satan whom the people fight in order to keep themselves alive. If they cease struggling against me, slothfulness will deaden their minds and hearts and souls, in accordance with the weird penalties of their tremendous myth.

'I am the enraged and mute tempest who agitates the minds of man and the hearts of women. And in fear of me, they will travel to places of worship to condemn me, or to places of vice to make me happy by surrendering to my will. The monk who prays in the silence of the night to keep me away from his bed is like the prostitute who invites me to her chamber. I am Satan everlasting and eternal.

'I am the builder of convents and monasteries upon the foundation of fear. I build wine shops and wicked houses upon the foundations of lust and self-gratification. If I cease to exist, fear and enjoyment will be abolished from the world, and through their disappearance, desires and hopes will cease to exist in the human heart. Life will become empty and cold, like a harp with broken strings. I am Satan everlasting.

'I am the inspiration for falsehood, slander, treachery, deceit and mockery, and if these elements were to be removed from this world, human society would become like a deserted field in which naught would thrive but thorns of virtue. I am Satan everlasting.

'I am the father and mother of sin, and if sin were to vanish, the fighters of sin would vanish with it, along with their families and structures.

'I am the heart of all evil. Would you wish for human

motion to stop through cessation of my heartbeats? Would you accept the result after destroying the cause? I am the cause! Would you allow me to die in this deserted wilderness? Do you desire to sever the bond that exists between you and me? Answer me, clergyman!'

And Satan stretched his arms and bent his head forward and gasped deeply; his face turned to grey and he resembled one of those Egyptian statues laid waste by the ages at the side of the Nile. Then he fixed his glittering eyes upon Father Samaan's face, and said, in a faltering voice, 'I am tired and weak. I did wrong by using my waning strength to speak on things you already knew. Now you may do as you please. You may carry me to your home and treat my wounds, or leave me in this place to die.'

Father Samaan quivered and rubbed his hands nervously, and with apology in his voice he said, 'I know now what I had not known an hour ago. Forgive my ignorance. I know that your existence in this world creates temptation, and temptation is a measurement by which God adjudges the value of human souls. It is a scale which Almighty God uses to weigh the spirits. I am certain that if you die, temptation will die, and with its passing, death will destroy the ideal power which elevates and alerts man.

'You must live, for if you die and the people know it, their fear of hell will vanish and they will cease worshipping, for naught would be sin. You must live, for in your life is the salvation of humanity from vice and sin.

'As to myself, I shall sacrifice my hatred for you on the altar of my love for man.'

Satan uttered a laugh that rocked the ground, and he said, 'What an intelligent person you are, Father! And what wonderful knowledge you possess in theological facts!

You have found, through the power of your knowledge, a purpose for my existence which I had never understood, and now we realize our need for each other.

'Come close to me, my brother; darkness is submerging the plains, and half of my blood has escaped upon the sand of this valley, and naught remains of me but the remnants of a broken body which death shall soon buy unless you render aid.' Father Samaan rolled the sleeves of his robe and approached, and lifted Satan to his back and walked towards his home.

In the midst of those valleys, engulfed with silence and embellished with the veil of darkness, Father Samaan walked towards the village with his back bent under his heavy burden. His black raiment and long beard were spattered with blood streaming from above him, but he struggled forward, his lips moving in fervent prayer for the life of the dying Satan.   *1 T*, 41–57

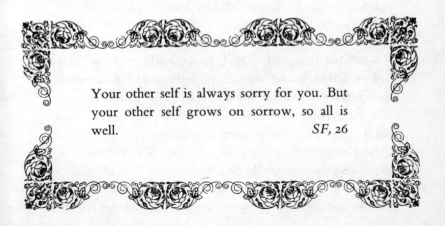

Your other self is always sorry for you. But your other self grows on sorrow, so all is well.   *SF*, 26

THE FROGS

Upon a summer day a frog said to his mate, 'I fear those people living in that house on the shore are disturbed by our night-songs.'

And his mate answered and said, 'Well, do they not annoy our silence during the day with their talking?'

The frog said, 'Let us not forget that we may sing too much in the night.'

And his mate answered, 'Let us not forget that they chatter and shout overmuch during the day.'

Said the frog, 'How about the bullfrog who disturbs the whole neighbourhood with his God-forbidden booming?'

And his mate replied, 'Aye, and what say you of the politician and the priest and the scientist who come to these shores and fill the air with noisy and rhymeless sound?'

Then the frog said, 'Well, let us be better than these human beings. Let us be quiet at night, and keep our songs in our hearts, even though the moon calls for our rhythm and the stars for our rhyme. At least, let us be silent for a night or two, or even for three nights.'

And his mate said, 'Very well, I agree. We shall see what your bountiful heart will bring forth.'

That night the frogs were silent; and they were silent the following night also, and again upon the third night.

And strange to relate, the talkative woman who lived in the house beside the lake came down to breakfast on that third day and shouted to her husband, 'I have not slept these three nights. I was secure with sleep when the noise of the frogs was in my ear. But something must have happened. They have not sung now for three nights; and I am almost maddened with sleeplessness.'

The frog heard this and turned to his mate and said, winking his eye, 'And we were almost maddened with our silence, were we not?'

And his mate answered, 'Yes, the silence of the night was heavy upon us. And I can see now that there is no need for us to cease our singing for the comfort of those who must needs fill their emptiness with noise.'

And that night the moon called not in vain for their rhythm nor the stars for their rhyme. *W*, 44–6

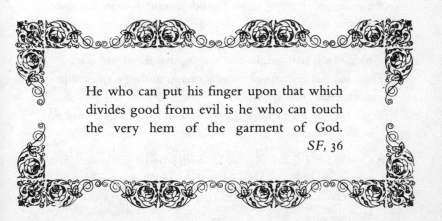

He who can put his finger upon that which divides good from evil is he who can touch the very hem of the garment of God. *SF,* 36

THE POET

An exile am I in this world.

An exile am I and alone, tormented by my aloneness, which ever directs my thought to a magic and unknown realm

And fills my dreams with shadows of a region distant and unseen.

An exile am I from my kinsmen and my countrymen, and should I meet one of them, I would say to myself:

'Who, then, is this one? Where is it I have known him?

What bond unites me to him, and why do I draw near to sit beside him?'

An exile am I from myself, and should I hear my own tongue speak, my ear finds the voice strange.

Sometimes I look within and behold my secret self, a hidden self that laughs and weeps, that dares and fears.

Then my being marvels at my being, and my spirit questions mine own spirit.

Yet I remain an exile, unknown, lost in the mist, clothed with the silence.

An exile am I from my body; and when I pause before a mirror, behold, in my face is that which my soul has not conceived, and in my eyes that which my depths do not contain.

When I walk upon the streets of the city, the children
  follow after me, shouting:
'Behold the blind man! Let us give him a staff to lean
  upon.'
And in haste I flee from them.
If I meet a bevy of maidens, they cleave to my garments,
  singing:
'He is deaf as a rock! Let us fill his ear with harmonies of
  love and passion.'
And from them I flee also.
Whenever I approach the middle-aged in the market-place,
  they gather about me, crying:
'He is as mute as a tomb! Let us straighten his twisted
  tongue.'
And I hasten from them in fear.
And if I pass by a company of elders, they point their
  trembling fingers towards me, saying:
'He is a madman who has lost his reason in the land of the
  Djinns and Ghouls!'

An exile am I in this world.
An exile am I, for I have traversed the earth both East and
  West,
Yet I found not my birthplace, nor one who knew me or
  had heard my name.
In the morning I awake to find myself imprisoned in a
  darkened cavern
Where vipers threaten from above, and every crawling
  thing infests the walls and ground.
When I seek the outer light, the shadows of my body
  march ahead of me –

Whereto I know not, seeking that I do not understand, grasping that for which I have no need.

When eventide is come and I return and lie upon my bed of thorn and feather,

Strange thoughts beguile me, both fearsome and joyous, and desires besiege me with their pains and their delights.

When it is midnight, the shades of bygone ages fall upon me, and spirits of forgotten regions visit me and look upon me,

And I gaze also upon them, and speak to them and ask of ancient things,

And with kindliness and smiles they answer me.

But when I would hold them and keep them, they escape me

And fade as they were but smoke upon the air.

An exile am I in this world.

An exile am I, and no man understands the language of my soul.

I pace the wilderness and I behold the rivulets climbing from the depths of the valley to the mountain top;

Before my eyes the naked trees come into bloom and bear their fruit and scatter their dead leaves, all in one moment.

And before my eyes their boughs fall to the lowland and are turned into dark serpents.

Ay, strange are my visions, like unto the visions of no man,

For I see birds lifting their wings unto the morning with songs, and then with lamentation;

I see them alight and change before my eyes into nude women with long, loosened hair

Who gaze at me from behind eyelids painted for love, and
    who smile upon me with lips dipped in honey,
And who stretch white hands to me, perfumed with frankin-
    cense and myrrh.
And even as I gaze, they vanish like a shaken mist,
Leaving in space the echo of their mocking laughter.

An exile am I in this world.
A poet am I who gathers in verse what life scatters in
    prose;
And scatters in prose what life gathers in verse.
And hence an exile am I, and an exile I shall remain until
    death lifts me up and bears me even unto my
    country.   *PP*, 69–74

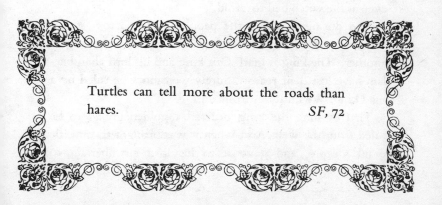

Turtles can tell more about the roads than
hares.   *SF,* 72

THE WISE KING

Once there ruled in the distant city of Wirani a king who was both mighty and wise. And he was feared for his might and loved for his wisdom.

Now, in the heart of that city was a well, whose water was cool and crystalline, from which all the inhabitants drank, even the king and his courtiers; for there was no other well.

One night when all were asleep, a witch entered the city, and poured seven drops of strange liquid into the well, and said, 'From this hour he who drinks this water shall become mad.'

Next morning all the inhabitants, save the king and his lord chamberlain, drank from the well and became mad, even as the witch had foretold.

And during that day the people in the narrow streets and in the market-places did naught but whisper to one another, 'The king is mad. Our king and his lord chamberlain have lost their reason. Surely we cannot be ruled by a mad king. We must dethrone him.'

That evening the king ordered a golden goblet to be filled from the well. And when it was brought to him, he drank deeply, and gave it to his lord chamberlain to drink.

And there was great rejoicing in that distant city of Wirani, because its king and its lord chamberlain had regained their reason.

M, 28–9

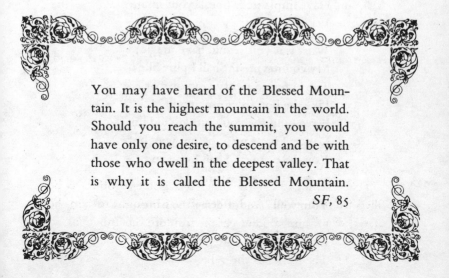

You may have heard of the Blessed Mountain. It is the highest mountain in the world. Should you reach the summit, you would have only one desire, to descend and be with those who dwell in the deepest valley. That is why it is called the Blessed Mountain.

SF, 85

MY COUNTRYMEN

What do you seek, my countrymen?
Do you desire that I build for
You gorgeous palaces, decorated
With words of empty meaning, or
Temples roofed with dreams? Or
Do you command me to destroy what
The liars and tyrants have built?
Shall I uproot with my fingers
What the hypocrites and the wicked
Have implanted? Speak your insane
Wish!

What is it you would have me do,
My countrymen? Shall I purr like
The kitten to satisfy you, or roar
Like the lion to please myself? I
Have sung for you, but you did not
Dance; I have wept before you, but
You did not cry. Shall I sing and
Weep at the same time?

Your souls are suffering the pangs
Of hunger, and yet the fruit of
Knowledge is more plentiful than
The stones of the valleys.

Your hearts are withering from
Thirst, and yet the springs of
Life are streaming about your
Homes – why do you not drink?
The sea has its ebb and flow,
The moon has its fullness and
Crescents, and the ages have
Their winter and summer, and all
Things vary like the shadow of
An unborn god moving between
Earth and sun, but truth cannot
Be changed, nor will it pass away;
Why, then, do you endeavour to
Disfigure its countenance?

I have called you in the silence
Of the night to point out the
Glory of the moon and the dignity
Of the stars, but you startled
From your slumber and clutched
Your swords in fear, crying,
'Where is the enemy? We must kill
Him first!' At morningtide, when
The enemy came, I called to you
Again, but now you did not wake
From your slumber, for you were
Locked in fear, wrestling with
The processions of spectres in
Your dreams.

And I said unto you, 'Let us climb
To the mountain top and view the
Beauty of the world.' And you

Answered me, saying, 'In the depths
Of this valley our fathers lived,
And in its shadows they died, and in
Its caves they were buried. How can
We depart this place for one which
They failed to honour?'
And I said unto you, 'Let us go to
The plain that gives its bounty to
The sea.' And you spoke timidly to
Me, saying, 'The uproar of the abyss
Will frighten our spirits, and the
Terror of the depths will deaden
Our bodies.'

I have loved you, my countrymen, but
My love for you is painful to me
And useless to you; and today I
Hate you, and hatred is a flood
That sweeps away the dry branches
And quavering houses.

I have pitied your weakness, my
Countrymen, but my pity has but
Increased your feebleness, exalting
And nourishing slothfulness which
Is vain to life. And today I see
Your infirmity which my soul loathes
And fears.

I have cried over your humiliation
And submission; and my tears streamed
Like crystalline, but could not sear
Away your stagnant weakness; yet they
Removed the veil from my eyes.

My tears have never reached your
Petrified hearts, but they cleansed
The darkness from my inner self.
Today I am mocking at your suffering,
For laughter is a raging thunder that
Precedes the tempest and never comes
After it.

What do you desire, my countrymen?
Do you wish for me to show you
The ghost of your countenance on
The face of still water? Come,
Now, and see how ugly you are!

Look and meditate! Fear has
Turned your hair grey as the
Ashes, and dissipation has grown
Over your eyes and made them into
Obscured hollows, and cowardice
Has touched your cheeks that now
Appear as dismal pits in the
Valley, and death has kissed
Your lips and left them yellow
As the autumn leaves.

What is it that you seek, my
Countrymen? What ask you from
Life, who does not any longer
Count you among her children?

Your souls are freezing in the
Clutches of the priests and
Sorcerers, and your bodies
Tremble between the paws of the

Despots and the shedders of
Blood, and your country quakes
Under the marching feet of the
Conquering enemy; what may you
Expect even though you stand
Proudly before the face of the
Sun? Your swords are sheathed
With rust, and your spears are
Broken, and your shields are
Laden with gaps; why, then, do
You stand in the field of battle?

Hypocrisy is your religion, and
Falsehood is your life, and
Nothingness is your ending; why,
Then, are you living? Is not
Death the sole comfort of the
Miserable?

Life is a resolution that
Accompanies youth, and a diligence
That follows maturity, and a
Wisdom that pursues senility; but
You, my countrymen, were born old
And weak. And your skins withered
And your heads shrank, whereupon
You became as children, running
Into the mire and casting stones
Upon each other.

Knowledge is a light, enriching
The warmth of life, and all may
Partake who seek it out; but you,

My countrymen, seek out darkness
And flee the light, awaiting the
Coming of water from the rock,
And your nation's misery is your
Crime. I do not forgive you
Your sins, for you know what you
Are doing.

Humanity is a brilliant river
Singing its way and carrying with
It the mountains' secrets into
The heart of the sea; but you,
My countrymen, are stagnant
Marshes infested with insects
And vipers.

The spirit is a sacred blue
Torch, burning and devouring
The dry plants, and growing
With the storm and illuminating
The faces of the goddesses; but
You, my countrymen, your souls
Are like ashes which the winds
Scatter upon the snow, and which
The tempests disperse forever in
The valleys.

Fear not the phantom of death,
My countrymen, for his greatness
And mercy will refuse to approach
Your smallness; and dread not the
Dagger, for it will decline to be
Lodged in your shallow hearts.

I hate you, my countrymen, because
You hate glory and greatness. I
Despise you because you despise
Yourselves. I am your enemy, for
You refuse to realize that you are
The enemies of the goddesses.   *1 T*, 159–65

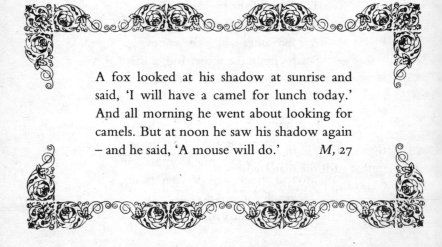

A fox looked at his shadow at sunrise and
said, 'I will have a camel for lunch today.'
And all morning he went about looking for
camels. But at noon he saw his shadow again
– and he said, 'A mouse will do.'   *M*, 27

THE POMEGRANATE

Once when I was living in the heart of a pomegranate, I heard a seed saying, 'Some day I shall become a tree, and the wind will sing in my branches, and the sun will dance on my leaves, and I shall be strong and beautiful through all the seasons.'

Then another seed spoke and said, 'When I was as young as you, I too held such views; but now that I can weigh and measure things, I see that my hopes were vain.'

And a third seed spoke also: 'I see in us nothing that promises so great a future.'

And a fourth said, 'But what a mockery our life would be, without a greater future!'

Said a fifth, 'Why dispute what we shall be, when we know not even what we are?'

But a sixth replied, 'Whatever we are, that we shall continue to be.'

And a seventh said, 'I have such a clear idea how everything will be, but I cannot put it into words.'

Then an eighth spoke – and a ninth – and a tenth – and then many – until all were speaking, and I could distinguish nothing for the many voices.

And so I moved that very day into the heart of a quince, where the seeds are few and almost silent.   *M*, 36–7

THE SILVER-PLATED TURD

Silman Effandi is a well-dressed man, tall and handsome, thirty-five years of age. He curls his moustaches and wears silk socks and patent-leather shoes. In his soft and delicate hand he carries a gold-headed and bejewelled walking-stick. He eats in the most expensive restaurants where the fashionable forgather. In his magnificent carriage, drawn by thoroughbreds, he rides through the upper-class boulevards.

Silman Effandi's wealth was not inherited from his father, who (may his soul rest in peace) was a poor man. Neither did Silman Effandi amass wealth by shrewd and persevering business activities. He is lazy and hates to work, regarding any form of labour as degrading.

Once we heard him say, 'My physique and temperament unfit me for work; work is meant for those with sluggish character and brutish body.'

Then how did Silman attain his riches? By what magic was the dirt in his hands transformed into gold and silver? This is a secret hidden in a silver-plated turd which Azrael, the angel of death, has revealed to us, and we in turn shall reveal it to you:

Five years ago Silman Effandi married the lady Fahima, widow of Betros Namaan, famous for his honesty, perseverance, and hard work.

Fahima was then forty-five years of age, but only sweet sixteen in her thoughts and behaviour. She now dyes her hair and by the use of cosmetics deludes herself that she remains young and beautiful. She does not see Silman, her young husband, except after midnight when he vouchsafes her a scornful look and some vulgarities and abuse by way of conversation. This entitles him, he believes, to spend the money which her first husband earned by the sweat of his brow.

Adib Effandi is a young man, twenty-seven years of age, blessed with a big nose, small eyes, dirty face and ink-spotted hands with filth-encrusted fingernails. His clothes are frayed and adorned with oil, grease and coffee stains.

His ugly appearance is not due to Adib Effandi's poverty but to his preoccupation with spiritual and theological ideas. He often quotes Amin El Jundy's saying that a scholar cannot be both clean and intelligent.

In his incessant talk Adib Effandi has nothing to say except to deliver judgement on others. On investigation, we found that Adib Effandi had spent two years in a school at Beirut studying rhetoric. He wrote poems, essays, and articles, which never saw print. His reasons for failing to achieve publication are the degeneration of the Arabic press and the ignorance of the Arabic reading public.

Recently Adib Effandi has been occupying himself with the study of the old and new philosophy. He admires Socrates and Nietzsche, and relishes the sayings of Saint Augustine as well as Voltaire and Rousseau. At a wedding party we heard him discussing Hamlet; but his talk was a soliloquy, for the others preferred to drink and sing.

On another occasion, at a funeral, the subjects of his talk

were the love poems of Ben Al Farid and the wine-ism of Abi Nawaas. But the mourners ignored him, being oppressed by grief.

Why, we often wonder, does Adib Effandi exist? What use are his rotting books and his parchments falling into dust? Would it not be better for him to buy himself an ass and become a healthy and useful ass-driver?

This is a secret hidden in the silver-plated turd revealed to us by Baal-Zabul and we in turn shall now reveal it to you:

Three years ago Adib Effandi composed a poem in praise of His Excellency, Bishop Joseph Shamoun. His Excellency placed his hand on the shoulder of Adib Effandi, smiled and said, 'Bravo, my son, God bless you! I have no doubt about your intelligence; some day you will be among the great men of the East.'

Farid Bey Davis is a man in his late thirties, tall, with a small head and large mouth, narrow forehead and a bald pate. He walks with a pompous rolling gait, swelling his chest and stretching his long neck like a camel.

From his loud voice and his haughty manner you might imagine him (provided you had not met him before) the minister of a great empire, absorbed in public affairs.

But Farid has nothing to do aside from enumerating and glorifying the deeds of his ancestors. He is fond of citing exploits of famous men, and deeds of heroes such as Napoleon and Antar. He is a collector of weapons of which he has never learned the use.

One of his sayings is that God created two different classes of people: the leaders and those who serve them. Another is that the people are like stubborn asses who do not stir unless you whip them. Another, that the pen was meant for the weak and the sword for the strong.

What prompts Farid to boast of his ancestry and behave as he does? This is a secret hidden in the silver-plated turd which Satanael has revealed to us, and we, in turn, reveal to you:

In the third decade of the nineteenth century, when Emir Bashir, the great governor of Mount Lebanon, was passing with his retinue through the Lebanese valleys, they approached the village in which Mansour Davis, Farid's grandfather, lived. It was an exceedingly hot day, and the emir dismounted from his horse and ordered his men to rest in the shadow of an oak tree.

Mansour Davis, discovering the emir's presence, called the neighbouring farmers, and the good news spread through the village. Led by Mansour the villagers brought baskets of grapes and figs, and jars of honey, wine and milk for the emir. When they reached the oak tree, Mansour kneeled before the emir and kissed the hem of his robe. Then he stood up and killed a sheep in the emir's honour, saying, 'The sheep is from thy bounty, oh prince and protector of our lives.' The emir, pleased with such hospitality, said to him, 'Henceforth you shall be the mayor of this village, which I will exempt from taxes for this year.'

That night, after the emir had left, the villagers met at the house of 'Sheik' Mansour Davis and vowed loyalty to the newly appointed sheik. May God have mercy on their souls.

There are too many secrets contained in the silver-plated turd to enumerate them all. The devils and satans reveal some to us every day and night, which we shall share with you before the angel of death wraps us under his wings and takes us into the great beyond.

Since it is now midnight and our eyes are getting heavy, permit us to surrender ourselves to slumber and perhaps the beautiful bride of dreams will carry our souls into a world cleaner than this one.   *TM*, 47–51

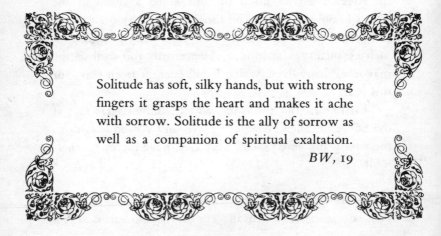

Solitude has soft, silky hands, but with strong fingers it grasps the heart and makes it ache with sorrow. Solitude is the ally of sorrow as well as a companion of spiritual exaltation.

BW, 19

The art of the Egyptians is in the occult.
The art of the Chaldeans is in calculation.
The art of the Greeks is in proportion.
The art of the Romans is in echo.
The art of the Chinese is in etiquette.
The art of the Hindus is in the weighing of good and evil.
The art of the Jews is in the sense of doom.
The art of the Arabs is in reminiscence and exaggeration.
The art of the Persians is in fastidiousness.
The art of the French is in finesse.
The art of the English is in analysis and self-righteousness.
The art of the Spaniards is in fanaticism.
The art of the Italians is in beauty.
The art of the Germans is in ambition.
The art of the Russians is in sadness.   *SS*, 33

THE CRIMINAL

A young man of strong body, weakened by hunger, sat on the walker's portion of the street stretching his hand towards all who passed, begging and repeating the sad song of his defeat in life, while suffering from hunger and from humiliation.

When night came, his lips and tongue were parched, while his hand was still as empty as his stomach.

He gathered himself and went out from the city, where he sat under a tree and wept bitterly. Then he lifted his puzzled eyes to heaven while hunger was eating his inside, and he said, 'Oh Lord, I went to the rich man and asked for employment, but he turned away because of my shabbiness; I knocked at the school door, but was forbidden solace because I was empty-handed; I sought any occupation that would give me bread, but all to no avail. In desperation I asked alms, but Thy worshippers saw me and said, "He is strong and lazy, and he should not beg."

'Oh Lord, it is Thy will that my mother gave birth unto me, and now the earth offers me back to You before the ending.'

His expression then changed. He arose and his eyes now glittered in determination. He fashioned a thick and heavy stick from the branch of the tree, and pointed it towards the city, shouting, 'I asked for bread with all the strength of my voice, and was refused. Now I shall obtain it by the strength of my muscles! I asked for bread in the name of mercy and love, but humanity did not heed. I shall take it now in the name of evil!'

The passing years rendered the youth a robber, killer, and destroyer of souls; he crushed all who opposed him; he amassed fabulous wealth, with which he won himself over to those in power. He was admired by colleagues, envied by other thieves, and feared by the multitudes.

His riches and false position prevailed upon the emir to appoint him deputy in that city – the sad process pursued by unwise governors. Thefts were then legalized; oppression was supported by authority; crushing of the weak became commonplace; the throngs curried and praised.

Thus does the first touch of humanity's selfishness make criminals of the humble, and make killers of the sons of peace; thus does the early greed of humanity grow and strike back at humanity a thousandfold!   *1 T*, 109–10

LAWS AND LAW-GIVING

Ages ago there was a great king, and he was wise. And he desired to lay laws unto his subjects.

He called upon one thousand wise men of one thousand different tribes to come to his capital and lay down the laws.

And all this came to pass.

But when the thousand laws written upon parchment were put before the king and he read them, he wept bitterly in his soul, for he had not known that there were one thousand forms of crime in his kingdom.

Then he called his scribe, and with a smile upon his mouth he himself dictated laws. And his laws were but seven.

And the one thousand wise men left him in anger and returned to their tribes with the laws they had laid down. And every tribe followed the laws of its wise men.

Therefore they have a thousand laws even to our own day.

It is a great country, but it has one thousand prisons, and the prisons are full of women and men, breakers of a thousand laws.

It is indeed a great country, but the people thereof are descendants of one thousand law-givers and of only one wise king.   *W*, 47–8

THE DANCER

Once there came to the court of the prince of Birkasha a dancer with her musicians. And she was admitted to the court, and she danced before the prince to the music of the lute and the flute and the zither.

She danced the dance of flames, and the dance of swords and spears; she danced the dance of stars and the dance of space. And then she danced the dance of flowers in the wind.

After this she stood before the throne of the prince and bowed her body before him. And the prince bade her to come nearer, and he said unto her, 'Beautiful woman, daughter of grace and delight, whence comes your art? And how is it that you command all the elements in your rhythms and your rhymes?'

And the dancer bowed again before the prince, and she answered, 'Mighty and gracious Majesty, I know not the answer to your questionings. Only this I know: the philosopher's soul dwells in his head, the poet's soul is in his heart; the singer's soul lingers about his throat, but the soul of the dancer abides in all her body.'   *W*, 32–3

THE CURSE

An old man of the sea once said to me, 'It was thirty years ago that a sailor ran away with my daughter. And I cursed them both in my heart, for of all the world I loved but my daughter.

'Not long after that, the sailor youth went down with his ship to the bottom of the sea, and with him my lovely daughter was lost unto me.

'Now therefore behold in me the murderer of a youth and a maid. It was my curse that destroyed them. And now on my way to the grave I seek God's forgiveness.'

This the old man said. But there was a tone of bragging in his word, and it seems that he is still proud of the power of his curse.   *W*, 70

THE SEVEN SELVES

In the stillest hour of the night, as I lay half asleep, my seven selves sat together and thus conversed in whispers:

First Self: Here, in this madman, I have dwelt all these years, with naught to do but renew his pain by day and recreate his sorrow by night. I can bear my fate no longer, and now I rebel.

Second Self: Yours is a better lot than mine, brother, for it is given me to be this madman's joyous self. I laugh his laughter and sing his happy hours, and with thrice-winged feet I dance his brighter thoughts. It is I that would rebel against my weary existence.

Third Self: And what of me, the love-ridden self, the flaming brand of wild passion and fantastic desires? It is I, the love-sick self, who would rebel against this madman.

Fourth Self: I, amongst you all, am the most miserable, for naught was given me but odious hatred and destructive loathing. It is I, the tempest-like self, the one born·in the black caves of hell, who would protest against serving this madman.

Fifth Self: Nay, it is I, the thinking self, the fanciful self, the self of hunger and thirst, the one doomed to wander without rest in search of unknown things and things not yet created; it is I, not you, who would rebel.

Sixth Self: And I, the working self, the pitiful labourer,

who, with patient hands and longing eyes, fashion the days into images and give the formless elements new and eternal forms – it is I, the solitary one, who would rebel against this restless madman.

Seventh Self: How strange that you would all rebel against this man, because each and every one of you has a pre-ordained fate to fulfil. Ah! could I but be like one of you, a self with a determined lot! But I have none. I am the do-nothing self, the one who sits in the dumb, empty nowhere and nowhen, while you are busy recreating life. Is it you or I, neighbours, who should rebel?

When the seventh self thus spoke, the other six selves looked with pity upon him, but said nothing more; and as the night grew deeper, one after another went to sleep enfolded with a new and happy submission.

But the seventh self remained watching and gazing at nothingness, which is behind all things.   *M,* 21–3

He who does not see the angels and devils in the beauty and malice of life will be far removed from knowledge, and his spirit will be empty of affection.   *BW,* 20

SECRETS OF THE HEART

In a fine palace standing in the dark night like life in the shadow of death a maiden sat in a chair of ivory. Her head was supported by her hand in the manner of a withered flower leaning upon its petals. She looked about her like a prisoner without hope who would pierce the prison wall with his eyes to look at life ever moving in the procession of freedom.

The hours passed as phantoms in the darkness, while the maiden solaced herself with tears and took refuge in her solitude and grief. And when the violence of her feeling became heavy on her heart and unlocked the treasury of her secret thoughts, she took up a pen, and her tears flowed with the ink. And she wrote thus:

'Beloved sister: When the heart is straitened with that which it conceals and eyelids are oppressed with tears and ribs are nigh torn asunder with growing hidden things, what is there for man save speech and complaint? The saddened deems complaint a sweet thing, and the lover finds consolation in the fire of his youth, and the oppressed sees relief in supplication. Now do I write to you thus because I am become a poet who beholds the beauty of all things and arranges the pattern of that beauty impelled by the power of his divineness. Or as a starveling child seeing succour, driven by the bitterness of its hunger, unmindful of its mother's poverty and destitution.

'Hearken to my pitiful tale, my sister, and weep for me. For weeping is like prayer, and the tears of compassion are as a good deed that goes not unrequited; they ascend from the depths of the spirit, a living thing. My father joined me in marriage with a man of riches and station, the like of all fathers of possessions and honour who wish to propagate wealth by wealth; fearing poverty and embracing honour with honour as a refuge from the shame of days. And so I and my dreams and longings were sacrificed on an altar of gold that I held as naught; to high estate, which was hateful in my sight. I was a prey trembling in the grasp of matter which, if it be not made to serve the spirit, is harsher than death and bitterer than the grave. I hold in esteem my lord, for he is generous and honourable and strives in the way of my happiness and pursues riches for my delight. But I have found that all these things are not worth one moment of a true and sanctified love; that love which holds as naught all things and remains mighty.

'Do not mock at me, my sister, for I am now become the most knowing of people in the things of a woman's heart, that palpitating heart, that bird fluttering in the firmament of love. That vessel overflowing with the wine of ages prepared for the lips of the soul. That book wherein are writ chapters of joy and grief; happiness and misery; pleasure and pain. That book none shall read save the true companion, the half of woman that is created for her from the beginning to the end of time.

'Ay, I have known women in their longings and desires since I saw that my lord's fine horses and carriages and his ever-filled coffers and high estate were not the equal of one glance from the eyes of a poor youth who entered this existence for my sake and for whom I did come. A patient one waiting in grief and the wretchedness of separation. An oppressed one sacrified to my father's will; imprisoned without guilt in the dungeons of time. Seek not to console me, for out of my affliction is a consoler, the knowledge of my love's power and the honour of my yearning and longing. I look now from beyond my tears and behold my lot, day by day, drawing nigh to lead me whither I shall await the companion of my spirit and meet with him and embrace him in a long and sacred embrace. Reproach me not, for I do as is proper to a faithful wife, submitting to the laws and customs of men with forbearance and enduring. I honour my lord and esteem him and laud him, but I am not capable of giving him my all, for God has already granted that to my beloved ere I knew him. Heaven has willed in its hidden wisdom that I pass my days with a man other than the one for whom I was created, and I shall pass this existence in silence in accordance with heaven's willing. And when the doors of eternity are open and I am joined with the half of my spirit, I shall look back upon the past – and the past is this very present – as does the spring on winter. I shall ponder on this life as one who has gained the summit considers the passes through which he has come ere attaining it.'

Here the maid ceased from writing. She covered her face with her hands and gave herself to bitter weeping as though her great spirit rebelled against the committing to paper of the holiest of her secrets. She dried her tears quickly and they were gone to abide in the gentle air, the resting-place of the souls of lovers and flowers.

After a while she took up again her pen and wrote:

'Do you remember that youth, my sister? Do you

remember the light shining from his eyes, and the sadness impressed upon his brow, and his smile that was like the tears of a bereaved woman? Do you recall his voice, which was as the echo of a far-off valley? Do you call him to memory when he would ponder on things with a long, silent look, and speak of them in wonder, and incline his head and sigh as though in fear that speech would betray what was concealed in his depths? And his dreams and beliefs, those too do you remember? Ay, these many things in a youth whom other men thought their like, whom my father did despise because he was raised above dross and more honourable than that he should inherit honour from his forebears.

'Ay, my sister, well do you know that I am a martyr of the small things of this world and a sacrifice to folly. Show pity to your sister, who sits up in the silent watches of the night to uncover to you the secrets of her breast. Have compassion, for love did likewise visit your heart.'

Morning came and the maiden rose from her writing and soon sleep overtook her. Mayhap she would find therein dreams sweeter than the dreams of awakening. *TS*, 108–12

THE OLD, OLD WINE

Once there lived a rich man who was justly proud of his cellar and the wine therein. And there was one jug of ancient vintage kept for some occasion known only to himself.

The governor of the state visited him, and he bethought him and said, 'That jug shall not be opened for a mere governor.'

And a bishop of the diocese visited him, but he said to himself, 'Nay, I will not open that jug. He would not know its value, nor would its aroma reach his nostrils.'

The prince of the realm came and supped with him. But he thought, 'It is too royal a wine for a mere princeling.'

And even on the day when his own nephew was married, he said to himself, 'No, not to these guests shall that jug be brought forth.'

And the years passed by, and he died, an old man, and he was buried like unto every seed and acorn.

And upon the day that he was buried the ancient jug was brought out together with other jugs of wine, and it was shared by the peasants of the neighbourhood. And none knew its great age.

To them, all that is poured into a cup is only wine. *W*, 62–3

THE RED EARTH

Said a tree to a man, 'My roots are in the deep red earth, and I shall give you of my fruit.'

And the man said to the tree, 'How alike we are. My roots are also deep in the red earth. And the red earth gives you power to bestow upon me of your fruit, and the red earth teaches me to receive from you with thanksgiving.'   *W*, 58

UPON THE SAND

Said one man to another, 'At the high tide of the sea, long ago, with the point of my staff I wrote a line upon the sand; and the people still pause to read it, and they are careful that naught shall erase it.'

And the other man said, 'And I too wrote a line upon the sand, but it was at low tide, and the waves of the vast sea washed it away. But tell me, what did you write?'

And the first man answered and said, 'I wrote this: "I am he who is." But what did you write?'

And the other man said, 'This I wrote: "I am but a drop of this great ocean."' *W*, 27

THE PEARL

Said one oyster to a neighbouring oyster, 'I have a very great pain within me. It is heavy and round, and I am in distress.'

And the other oyster replied with haughty complacence, 'Praise be to the heavens and to the sea, I have no pain within me. I am well and whole both within and without.'

At that moment a crab was passing by and heard the two oysters, and he said to the one who was well and whole both within and without, 'Yes, you are well and whole; but the pain that your neighbour bears is a pearl of exceeding beauty.' *W*, 20

THE SLEEP-WALKERS

In the town where I was born lived a woman and her daughter, who walked in their sleep.

One night, while silence enfolded the world, the woman and her daughter, walking, yet asleep, met in their mist-veiled garden.

And the mother spoke, and she said: 'At last, at last, my enemy! You by whom my youth was destroyed – who have built up your life upon the ruins of mine! Would I could kill you!'

And the daughter spoke, and she said: 'O hateful woman, selfish and old! Who stand between my freer self and me! Who would have my life an echo of your own failed life! Would you were dead!'

At that moment a cock crew, and both women awoke. The mother said gently,'Is that you, darling?' And the daughter answered gently, 'Yes, dear.' *M*, 15–16

BODY AND SOUL

A man and a woman sat by a window that opened upon spring. They sat close one unto the other. And the woman said, 'I love you. You are handsome, and you are rich, and you are always well attired.'

And the man said, 'I love you. You are a beautiful thought, a thing too apart to hold in the hand, and a song in my dreaming.'

But the woman turned from him in anger, and she said, 'Sir, please leave me now. I am not a thought, and I am not a thing that passes in your dreams. I am a woman. I would have you desire me, a wife, and the mother of unborn children.'

And they parted.

And the man was saying in his heart, 'Behold another dream is even now turned into the mist.'

And the woman was saying, 'Well, what of a man who turns me into mist and a dream?'   *W*, 21

SEVEN REASONS FOR
SELF-CONTEMPT

Seven times have I despised my soul:

The first time when I saw her being meek that she might attain height.

The second time when I saw her limping before the crippled.

The third time when she was given to choose between the hard and the easy, and she chose the easy.

The fourth time when she committed a wrong, and comforted herself that others also commit wrong.

The fifth time when she forbore for weakness, and attributed her patience to strength.

The sixth time when she despised the ugliness of a face, and knew not that it was one of her own masks.

And the seventh time when she sang a song of praise, and deemed it a virtue.   *SF*, 10

FAME

I walked upon the sand at ebb tide.
And bending down, I wrote a line upon the sand.
And in that line I wrote what my mind thought
And what my soul desired.

And when the tide was high,
I returned to that very shore,
And of that which I had written I found naught.
I found only the staff-marks of one who had walked
    blindly.   *PP*, 75

YOUR THOUGHT AND MINE

Your thought is a tree rooted deep in the soil of tradition and whose branches grow in the power of continuity.

My thought is a cloud moving in the space. It turns into drops which, as they fall, form a brook that sings its way into the sea. Then it rises as vapour into the sky.

Your thought is a fortress that neither gale nor the lightning can shake.

My thought is a tender leaf that sways in every direction and finds pleasure in its swaying.

Your thought is an ancient dogma that cannot change you nor can you change it.

My thought is new, and it tests me and I test it morn and eve.

You have your thought and I have mine.

Your thought allows you to believe in the unequal contest of the strong against the weak, and in the tricking of the simple by the subtle ones.

My thought creates in me the desire to till the earth with my hoe, and harvest the crops with my sickle, and build my home with stones and mortar, and weave my raiment with woollen and linen threads.

Your thought urges you to marry wealth and notability.

Mine commends self-reliance.

Your thought advocates fame and show.

Mine counsels me and implores me to cast aside notoriety and treat it like a grain of sand cast upon the shore of eternity.

Your thought instils in your heart arrogance and superiority.

Mine plants within me love for peace and the desire for independence.

Your thought begets dreams of palaces with furniture of sandalwood studded with jewels, and beds made of twisted silk threads.

My thought speaks softly in my ears, 'Be clean in body and spirit even if you have nowhere to lay your head.'

Your thought makes you aspire to titles and office.

Mine exhorts me to humble service.

You have your thought and I have mine.

Your thought is social science, a religious and political dictionary.

Mine is a simple axiom.

Your thought speaks of the beautiful woman, the ugly, the virtuous, the prostitute, the intelligent, and the stupid.

Mine sees in every woman a mother, a sister, or a daughter of every man.

The subjects of your thought are thieves, criminals, and assassins.

Mine declares that thieves are the creatures of monopoly, criminals are the offspring of tyrants, and assassins are akin to the slain.

Your thought describes laws, courts, judges, punishments.

Mine explains that when man makes a law, he either violates it or obeys it. If there is a basic law, we are all one before it. He who disdains the mean is himself mean. He who vaunts his scorn of the sinful vaunts his disdain of all humanity.

Your thought concerns the skilled, the artist, the intellectual, the philosopher, the priest.

Mine speaks of the loving and the affectionate, the sincere, the honest, the forthright, the kindly, and the martyr.

Your thought advocates Judaism, Brahmanism, Buddhism, Christianity, and Islam.

In my thought there is only one universal religion, whose varied paths are but the fingers of the loving hand of the Supreme Being.

In your thought there are the rich, the poor, and the beggared.

My thought holds that there are no riches but life; that we are all beggars, and no benefactor exists save life herself.

You have your thought and I have mine.

According to your thought, the greatness of nations lies in their politics, their parties, their conferences, their alliances and treaties.

But mine proclaims that the importance of nations lies in work – work in the field, work in the vineyards, work with the loom, work in the tannery, work in the quarry, work in the timberyard, work in the office and in the press.

Your thought holds that the glory of the nations is in their heroes. It sings the praises of Rameses, Alexander, Caesar, Hannibal, and Napoleon.

But mine claims that the real heroes are Confucius, Lao-Tse, Socrates, Plato, Abi Taleb, El Gazali, Jalal Ed-din-el Roumy, Copernicus, and Pasteur.

Your thought sees power in armies, cannons, battleships, submarines, aeroplanes, and poison gas.

But mine asserts that power lies in reason, resolution, and truth. No matter how long the tyrant endures, he will be the loser at the end.

Your thought differentiates between pragmatist and idealist, between the part and the whole, between the mystic and materialist.

Mine realizes that life is one and its weights, measures and tables do not coincide with your weights, measures and tables. He whom you suppose an idealist may be a practical man.

You have your thought and I have mine.

Your thought is interested in ruins and museums, mummies and petrified objects.

But mine hovers in the ever-renewed haze and clouds.

Your thought is enthroned on skulls. Since you take pride in it, you glorify it too.

My thought wanders in the obscure and distant valleys.

Your thought trumpets while you dance.

Mine prefers the anguish of death to your music and dancing.

Your thought is the thought of gossip and false pleasure.

Mine is the thought of him who is lost in his own country, of the alien in his own nation, of the solitary among his kinfolk and friends.

You have your thought and I have mine.   *SS*, 90–94

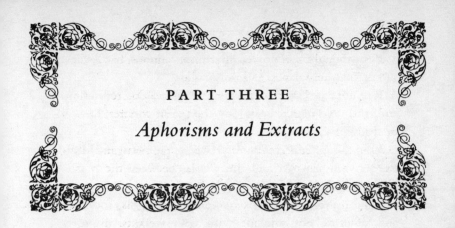

PART THREE

Aphorisms and Extracts

And what is word knowledge
but a shadow of wordless knowledge?
The Prophet, 112

ON GOD, FAITH AND RELIGION

God has made many doors opening into truth which He opens to all who knock upon them with hands of faith.   *1 T*, 138

Faith is an oasis in the heart which will never be reached by the caravan of thinking.   *SF*, 71

How ignorant are those who see, without question, the abstract existence with *some* of their senses, but insist upon doubting until that existence reveals itself to *all* of their senses! Is not faith the sense of the heart as truly as sight is the sense of the eye?   *1 T*, 148

Prayer is the song of the heart that makes its way to the throne of God even when entangled in the wailing of thousands of souls.   *SS*, 50

They say to me, 'You must needs choose between the pleasures of this world and the peace of the next world.' And I say to them, 'I have chosen both the delights of this world and the peace of the next. For I know in my heart that the Supreme Poet wrote but one poem, and it scans perfectly, and it also rhymes perfectly.'   *SF*, 71

If we were to do away with the various religions, we would find ourselves united and enjoying one great faith and religion, abounding in brotherhood.   *1T*, 135

Were a God to deny His blessing to those who pursue a different path to eternity, then there is no human who should offer worship.   *1T*, 142

Remember: one just man causes the devil greater affliction than a million blind believers.   *VM*, 62

You and I are all children of one faith, for the divers paths of religion are fingers of the loving hand of one Supreme Being, a hand extended to all, offering completeness of spirit to all, eager to receive all.   *VM*, 69

ON SOCIETY AND FREEDOM

Did God give us the breath of life to place it under death's feet? Did he give us liberty to make it a shadow for slavery? He who extinguishes his spirit's fire with his own hands is an infidel in the eyes of heaven, for heaven set the fire that burns in our spirits. He who does not rebel against oppression is doing himself injustice.   *BW*, 112

It is the mind that yields to the laws made by us, but never the spirit in us.   *SF*, 61

Human society has yielded for seventy centuries to corrupted laws until it cannot understand the meaning of the superior and eternal laws. A man's eyes have become accustomed to the dim light of candles and cannot see the sunlight. Spiritual disease is inherited from one generation to another, until it has become part of the people, who look upon it, not as a disease, but as a natural gift, showered by God upon Adam. If those people found someone free from the germs of this disease, they would think of him with shame and disgrace.   *BW*, 105–6

The bird has an honour that man does not have. Man lives in the traps of his fabricated laws and traditions, but the birds live according to the natural law of God, who causes the earth to turn around the sun.   *SS*, 49–50

ON BEAUTY

Beauty is that which attracts your soul, and that which loves to give and not to receive. *1 T*, 407

One hour devoted to the pursuit of Beauty
And Love is worth a full century of glory
Given by the frightened weak to the strong.

From that hour comes man's Truth; and
During that century Truth sleeps between
The restless arms of disturbing dreams.

In that hour the soul sees for herself
The Natural Law, and for that century she
Imprisons herself behind the law of man,
And she is shackled with irons of oppression. *1 T*, 411

Beauty reveals herself to us as she sits on the throne of glory; but we approach her in the name of lust, snatch off her crown of purity, and pollute her garment with our evil-doing. *VM*, 46

Poetry is not an opinion expressed. It is a song that rises from a bleeding wound or a smiling mouth.   *SF*, 21

A poet is a dethroned king sitting among the ashes of his palace, trying to fashion an image out of the ashes.   *SF*, 21

Poetry is wisdom that enchants the heart. Wisdom is poetry that sings in the mind. If we could enchant man's heart and at the same time sing in his mind, then in truth he would live in the shadow of God.   *SF*, 23

There lies a green field between the scholar and the poet; should the scholar cross it, he becomes a wise man; should the poet cross it, he becomes a prophet.   *SF*, 64

Poets are unhappy people, for no matter how high their spirits reach, they will still be enclosed in an envelope of tears.   *BW*, 41

Poetry is the understanding of the whole. How can you communicate it to him who understands but the part?   *SS*, 22

A singer cannot delight you with his singing unless he himself delights to sing.   *SS*, 23

Poetry is a flash of lightning; it becomes mere composition when it is an arrangement of words.   *SS*, 32

If you sing of beauty though alone in the heart of the desert, you will have an audience.   *SF*, 22

ON TRUTH

The truth that needs proof is only half true.   *SS*, 23

A truth is to be known always, to be uttered sometimes.   *SF*, 15

Truth is the will and purpose of God in man.   *SS*, 54

Truth visits us led by the smile of a child and a lover's kiss, and we close the door of our tenderness against her and abandon her as one unclean.   *TS*, 68

Many a doctrine is like a window pane. We see truth through it, but it divides us from truth.   *SF*, 17

He who does not seek advice is a fool. His folly blinds him
to truth and makes him evil, stubborn and a danger to his
fellow man.   *VM*, 67

ON LIFE

We live only to discover beauty. All else is a form of
waiting.   *SF*, 27

The voice of life in me cannot reach the ear of life in you;
but let us talk that we may not feel lonely.   *SF*, 15

When life does not find a singer to sing her heart, she
produces a philosopher to speak her mind.   *SF*, 15

We are all beggars at the gate of the temple, and each one
of us receives his share of the bounty of the king when he
enters the temple, and when he goes out. But we are all
jealous of one another, which is another way of belittling
the king.   *SF*, 32

God has placed in each soul a true guide to the great light, but man struggles to find life outside himself, unaware that the life he is seeking is within him.   *1 T*, 144

How beautiful is life, my beloved; it is like a poet's heart, filled with light and tenderness. And how cruel is life, my love; it is like a criminal's heart, throbbing with vice and fear.   *TM*, 67

ON WOMAN

Once I saw the face of a woman, and I beheld all her children not yet born. And a woman looked upon my face and she knew all my forefathers, dead before she was born. *SF*, 4

A woman's heart is like a field turned into a battleground; after the trees are uprooted and the grass is burned and the rocks are reddened with blood and the earth is planted with bones and skulls, it is calm and silent as if nothing has happened; for the spring and the autumn come at their intervals and resume their work. *BW*, 71

Men who do not forgive women their little faults will never enjoy their great virtues. *SF*, 28

The song that lies silent in the heart of a mother sings upon the lips of her child. *SF*, 25

A woman whom providence has provided with beauty of spirit and body is a truth, at the same time both open and secret, which we can understand only by love, and touch only by virtue; and when we attempt to describe such a woman she disappears like a vapour.   *BW*, 39–40

ON MAN

We were fluttering, wandering, longing creatures a thousand thousand years before the sea and the wind in the forest gave us words. Now how can we express the ancient of days in us with only the sounds of our yesterdays?   *SF*, 3

Man is empowered by God to hope and hope fervently, until that for which he is hoping takes the cloak of oblivion from his eyes, whereupon he will at last view his real self. And he who sees his real self sees the truth of real life for himself, for all humanity, and for all things.   *IT*, 140

The real in us is silent; the acquired is talkative.   *SF*, 15

God has created your spirits with wings to fly in the spacious firmament of love and freedom. How pitiful to lop off your wings with your own hands and suffer your spirit to crawl like vermin upon the earth!   *SS*, 55

The significance of man is not in what he attains, but rather in what he longs to attain.   *SF*, 12

I have been here since the beginning, and I shall be until the end of days; for there is no ending to my existence. The human soul is but a part of a burning torch which God separated from himself at creation.   *VM*, 67

Man merely discovers; he never can and never will invent.   *SS*, 44

ON LOVE

Love that does not renew itself every day becomes a habit and in turn a slavery. *SF*, 28

The chemist who can extract from his heart's elements compassion, respect, longing, patience, regret, surprise and forgiveness, and compound them into one, can create that atom which is called *love*. *SS*, 37

The heart's affections are divided like the branches of the cedar tree; if the tree loses one strong branch, it will suffer, but it does not die. It will pour all its vitality into the next branch, so that it will grow and fill the empty place. *BW*, 93–4

The space that lies between you and your near neighbour unbefriended is indeed greater than that which lies between you and your beloved who dwells beyond seven lands and seven seas. For in remembrance there are no distances; and only in oblivion is there a gulf that neither your voice nor your eye can abridge.   *GP*, 21–2

Love is the only freedom in the world, because it so elevates the spirit that the laws of humanity and the phenomena of nature do not alter its course.   *BW*, 35

Love passes by us, robed in meekness; but we flee from her in fear, or hide in the darkness; or else pursue her, to do evil in her name.   *VM*, 46

Passionate love is a quenchless thirst.   *SS*, 32

It is wrong to think that love comes from long companionship and persevering courtship. Love is the offspring of spiritual affinity and unless that affinity is created in a moment, it will not be created in years or. even generations.   *BW*, 52–3

Those whom love has not chosen as followers do not hear when love calls.   *BW*, 75

AN EDUCATIONAL IDEAL

Youth is a beautiful dream, but its sweetness is enslaved by the dullness of books and its awakening is a harsh one. Shall there come a day when wise men are able to unite the dreams of youth and the delights of learning, as reproach brings together hearts in conflict? Shall there come a day when man's teacher is nature, and humanity is his book and life his school? Will that day be? We know not, but we feel the urgency that moves us ever upwards towards a spiritual progress, and that progress is an understanding of the beauty of all creation through the kindness of ourselves and the dissemination of happiness through our love of that beauty.   *NV, 6–7*

MOTHER

The most beautiful word on the lips of mankind is the word 'Mother', and the most beautiful call is the call of 'My mother'. It is a word full of hope and love, a sweet and kind word coming from the depths of the heart. The mother is everything − she is our consolation in sorrow, our hope in misery, and our strength in weakness. She is the source of love, mercy, sympathy, and forgiveness. He who loses his mother loses a pure soul who blesses and guards him constantly.

Everything in nature bespeaks the mother. The sun is the mother of earth and gives it its nourishment of heat; it never leaves the universe at night until it has put the earth to sleep to the song of the sea and the hymn of birds and brooks. And this earth is the mother of trees and flowers. It produces them, nurses them, and weans them. The trees and flowers become kind mothers of their great fruits and seeds. And the mother, the prototype of all existence, is the eternal spirit, full of beauty and love . . . The word mother is hidden in our hearts, and it comes upon our lips in hours of sorrow and happiness as the perfume comes from the heart of the rose and mingles with clear and cloudy air. *BW*, 92–3

THE SPIRIT OF GOD ON EARTH

I love my native village with some of my love for my country; and I love my country with part of my love for the earth, all of which is my country; and I love the earth with all of myself because it is the haven of humanity, the manifest spirit of God.

Humanity is the spirit of the Supreme Being on earth, and that humanity is standing amidst ruins, hiding its nakedness behind tattered rags, shedding tears upon hollow cheeks, and calling for its children with pitiful voice. But the children are busy singing their clan's anthem; they are busy sharpening the swords and cannot hear the cry of their mothers.

Humanity appeals to its people but they listen not. Were one to listen, and console a mother by wiping her tears, others would say, 'He is weak, affected by sentiment.'

Humanity is the spirit of the Supreme Being on earth, and that Supreme Being preaches love and goodwill. But the people ridicule such teachings. The Nazarene Jesus listened, and crucifixion was his lot; Socrates heard the voice and followed it, and he too fell victim in body. The followers of the Nazarene and Socrates are the followers of deity, and since people will not kill them, they deride them, saying, 'Ridicule is more bitter than killing.'

Jerusalem could not kill the Nazarene, nor Athens Socrates; they are living yet and shall live eternally. Ridicule cannot triumph over the followers of deity. They live and grow forever.   *1 T*, 4–6

Between the people of eternity and the people of the earth there is a constant communication, and all comply with the will of that unseen power. Oftentimes an individual will perform an act, believing that it is born of his own free will, accord and command, but in fact he is being guided and impelled with precision to do it. Many great men attained their glory by surrendering themselves in complete submission to the will of the spirit, employing no reluctance or resistance to its demands, as a violin surrenders itself to the complete will of a fine musician.

Between the spiritual world and the world of substance there is a path upon which we walk in a swoon of slumber. It reaches us and we are unaware of its strength, and when we return to ourselves we find that we are carrying with our real hands the seeds to be planted carefully in the good earth of our daily lives, bringing forth good deeds and words of beauty. Were it not for that path between our lives and the departed lives, no prophet or poet or learned man would have appeared among the people. Truly I say unto you, and the outcome of time will prove it, that there are ties between the upper world and the lower world as surely as there is a binding tie between a mother and her child.

We are surrounded with an intuitive atmosphere that

attracts our inner consciousness, and a knowledge that
cautions our judgement, and a power that strengthens our
own power. I say unto you that our doubt does not
disprove or fortify our surrender to that which we doubt,
and the fact of busying ourselves in self-gratification will
not divert us from the accomplishment by the spirits of
their purpose; and blinding ourselves to the reality of our
spiritual being will not conceal our spiritual being from the
eyes of the universe; and if we stop walking, we are still
walking if they are walking . . . and if we remain motionless, we are still moving with their moving . . . and if we
silence ourselves, we are still speaking with their voices.

Our sleep cannot drive the influence of their awakeness
from us, nor can our awakeness divert their dreams from
the stages of our fancies, for we and they are two worlds
embraced by one world . . . we and they are two spirits
wrapped within one spirit . . . we and they are two exist-
ences united by one supreme and eternal consciousness
which is above all and without beginning and without
ending.   *1 T*, 146–7

LET ME GO PEACEFULLY

Let me go peacefully, my child. I have broken the bars of this cage; let me fly and do not stop me, for your mother is calling me. The sky is clear and the sea is calm and the boat is ready to sail; do not delay its voyage. Let my body rest with those who are resting; let my dream end and my soul awaken with the dawn; let your soul embrace mine and give me the kiss of hope; let no drops of sorrow or bitterness fall upon my body lest the flowers and grass refuse their nourishment. Do not shed tears of misery upon my hand, for they may grow thorns upon my grave. Do not draw lines of agony upon my forehead, for the wind may pass and read them and refuse to carry the dust of my bones to the green prairies. I loved you, my child, while I lived, and I shall love you when I am dead, and my soul shall always watch over you and protect you.

Do not call the physician, for he might extend my sentence in this prison by his medicine. The days of slavery are gone, and my soul seeks the freedom of the skies. And do not call the priest to my bedside, because his incantations would not save me if I were a sinner, nor would they rush me to heaven if I were innocent. The will of humanity cannot change the will of God, as an astrologer cannot change the course of the stars. But after my death let the doctors and priest do what they please, for my ship will continue sailing until it reaches its destination.   *BW*, 95–6

SLAVERY

Everything on earth lives according to the law of nature, and from that law emerges the glory and joy of liberty; but man is denied this fortune, because he set for the God-given soul a limited and earthly law of his own. He made for himself strict rules. Man built a narrow and painful prison in which he secluded his affections and desires. He dug out a deep grave in which he buried his heart and its purpose. If an individual, through the dictates of his soul, declares his withdrawal from society and violates the law, his fellow men will say he is a rebel worthy of exile, or an infamous creature worthy only of execution. Will man remain a slave of self-confinement until the end of the world? Or will he be freed by the passing of time and live in the spirit for the spirit? Will man insist upon staring downwards and backwards at the earth? Or will he turn his eyes towards the sun so he will not see the shadow of his body amongst the skulls and thorns?   *1T*, 228–9

MAN IS FOOD FOR THE GODS

Man is food for the gods,
And the glory of man begins
When his aimless breath is sucked by gods' hallowed lips.
All that is human counts for naught if human it remain,
The innocence of childhood, and the sweet ecstasy of
   youth,
The passion of stern manhood, and the wisdom of old age;
The splendour of kings and the triumph of warriors,
The fame of poets and the honour of dreamers and saints;
All these and all that lieth therein is bread for gods
And naught but bread ungraced shall it be
If the gods raise it not to their mouths.
And as the mute grain turns to love songs when swallowed
   by the nightingale,
Even so as bread for gods shall man taste
   godhead.   *EG*, 12–13

PART FOUR

Prophecies

Extracts from *The Prophet* and
The Garden of the Prophet

A great singer is he who sings our silences.
Sand and Foam, 24

THE PROPHET ON LOVE

When love beckons to you, follow him,
  Though his ways are hard and steep.
  And when his wings enfold you yield to him,
  Though the sword hidden among his pinions may wound you.
  And when he speaks to you believe in him,
  Though his voice may shatter your dreams as the north wind lays waste the garden.

For even as love crowns you so shall he crucify you.
  Even as he is for your growth so is he for your pruning.
  Even as he ascends to your height and caresses your tenderest branches that quiver in the sun,
  So shall he descend to your roots and shake them in their clinging to the earth.
  Like sheaves of corn he gathers you unto himself.
  He threshes you to make you naked.
  He sifts you to free you from your husks.
  He grinds you to whiteness.
  He kneads you until you are pliant;
  And then he assigns you to his sacred fire, that you may become sacred bread for God's sacred feast.

All these things shall love do unto you that you may know the secrets of your heart, and in that knowledge become a fragment of Life's heart.

But if in your fear you would seek only love's peace and
love's pleasure,

Then it is better for you that you cover your nakedness
and pass out of love's threshing-floor,

Into the seasonless world where you shall laugh, but not
all of your laughter, and weep, but not all of your tears.

Love gives naught but itself and takes naught but from
itself.

Love possesses not nor would it be possessed;

For love is sufficient unto love.

When you love you should not say, 'God is in my
heart,' but rather, 'I am in the heart of God.'

And think not you can direct the course of love, for
love, if it finds you worthy, directs your course.

Love has no other desire but to fulfil itself.

But if you love and must needs have desires, let these be
your desires:

To melt and be like a running brook that sings its
melody to the night.

To know the pain of too much tenderness.

To be wounded by your own understanding of love;

And to bleed willingly and joyfully.

To wake at dawn with a winged heart and give thanks
for another day of loving;

To rest at the noon hour and meditate love's ecstasy;

To return home at eventide with gratitude;

And then to sleep with a prayer for the beloved in your
heart and a song of praise upon your lips.   *P*, 11–17

THE PROPHET ON CHILDREN

Your children are not your children.

They are the sons and daughters of life's longing for itself.

They come through you but not from you,

And though they are with you yet they belong not to you.

You may give them your love but not your thoughts,

For they have their own thoughts.

You may house their bodies but not their souls,

For their souls dwell in the house of tomorrow, which you cannot visit, not even in your dreams.

You may strive to be like them, but seek not to make them like you.

For life goes not backwards nor tarries with yesterday.

You are the bows from which your children as living arrows are sent forth.

The archer sees the mark upon the path of the infinite, and he bends you with his might that his arrows may go swift and far.

Let your bending in the archer's hand be for gladness;

For even as he loves the arrow that flies, so he loves also the bow that is stable.   *P*, 22–5

THE PROPHET ON WORK

You work that you may keep pace with the earth and the soul of the earth.

For to be idle is to become a stranger unto the seasons, and to step out of life's procession that marches in majesty and proud submission towards the infinite.

When you work you are a flute through whose heart the whispering of the hours turns to music.

Which of you would be a reed, dumb and silent, when all else sings together in unison?

Always you have been told that work is a curse and labour a misfortune.

But I say to you that when you work you fulfil a part of earth's furthest dream, assigned to you when that dream was born,

And in keeping yourself with labour you are in truth loving life,

And to love life through labour is to be intimate with life's inmost secret.

But if you in your pain call birth an affliction and the support of the flesh a curse written upon your brow, then I answer that naught but the sweat of your brow shall wash away that which is written.

You have been told also that life is darkness, and in your weariness, you echo what was said by the weary.

And I say that life is indeed darkness save when there is urge,

And all urge is blind save when there is knowledge.

And all knowledge is vain save when there is work,

And all work is empty save when there is love;

And when you work with love you bind yourself to yourself, and to one another, and to God.

And what is it to work with love?

It is to weave the cloth with threads drawn from your heart, even as if your beloved were to wear that cloth.

It is to build a house with affection, even as if your beloved were to dwell in that house.

It is to sow seeds with tenderness and reap the harvest with joy, even as if your beloved were to eat the fruit.

It is to charge all things you fashion with a breath of your own spirit,

And to know that all the blessed dead are standing about you and watching.

Often have I heard you say, as if speaking in sleep, 'He who works in marble, and finds the shape of his own soul in the stone, is nobler than he who ploughs the soil.

'And he who seizes the rainbow, to lay it on a cloth in the likeness of man, is more than he who makes the sandals for our feet.'

But I say, not in sleep, but in the overwakefulness of noontide, that the wind speaks not more sweetly to the giant oaks than to the least of all the blades of grass;

And he alone is great who turns the voice of the wind into a song made sweeter by his own loving.

Work is love made visible.

And if you cannot work with love but only with distaste, it is better that you should leave your work and sit at the gate of the temple and take alms of those who work with joy.

For if you bake bread with indifference, you bake a bitter bread that feeds but half man's hunger.

And if you grudge the crushing of the grapes, your grudge distils a poison in the wine.

And if you sing though as angels, and love not the singing, you muffle man's ears to the voices of the day and the voices of the night.   *P*, 35–9

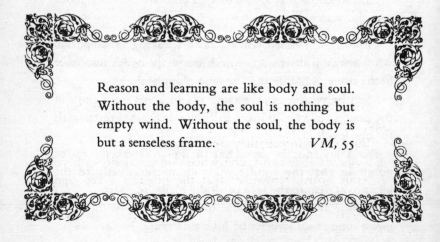

Reason and learning are like body and soul. Without the body, the soul is nothing but empty wind. Without the soul, the body is but a senseless frame.   *VM*, 55

THE PROPHET ON JOY
AND SORROW

Your joy is your sorrow unmasked.

And the selfsame well from which your laughter rises was oftentimes filled with your tears.

And how else can it be?

The deeper that sorrow carves into your being, the more joy you can contain.

Is not the cup that holds your wine the very cup that was burned in the potter's oven?

And is not the lute that soothes your spirit the very wood that was hollowed with knives?

When you are joyous, look deep into your heart and you shall find it is only that which has given you sorrow that is giving you joy.

When you are sorrowful, look again in your heart, and you shall see that in truth you are weeping for that which has been your delight.

Some of you say, 'Joy is greater than sorrow,' and others say, 'Nay, sorrow is the greater.'

But I say unto you, they are inseparable.

Together they come, and when one sits alone with you at your board, remember that the other is asleep upon your bed.

Verily you are suspended like scales between your sorrow and your joy.

Only when you are empty are you at standstill and balanced.

When the treasure-keeper lifts you to weigh his gold and his silver, needs must your joy or your sorrow rise or fall.   *P*, 40–41

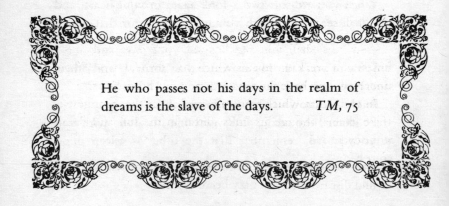

He who passes not his days in the realm of dreams is the slave of the days.   *TM*, 75

THE PROPHET ON FREEDOM

At the city gate and by your fireside I have seen you prostrate yourself and worship your own freedom,

Even as slaves humble themselves before a tyrant and praise him though he slays them.

Ay, in the grove of the temple and in the shadow of the citadel I have seen the freest among you wear their freedom as a yoke and a handcuff.

And my heart bled within me; for you can only be free when even the desire of seeking freedom becomes a harness to you, and when you cease to speak of freedom as a goal and a fulfilment.

You shall be free indeed when your days are not without a care nor your nights without a want and a grief,

But rather when these things girdle your life and yet you rise above them naked and unbound.

And how shall you rise beyond your days and nights unless you break the chains which you at the dawn of your understanding have fastened around your noon hour?

In truth that which you call freedom is the strongest of these chains, though its links glitter in the sun and dazzle your eyes.

And what is it but fragments of your own self you would discard that you may become free?

If it is an unjust law you would abolish, that law was written with your own hand upon your own forehead.

You cannot erase it by burning your law books nor by washing the foreheads of your judges, though you pour the sea upon them.

And if it is a despot you would dethrone, see first that his throne erected within you is destroyed.

For how can a tyrant rule the free and the proud, but for a tyranny in their own freedom and a shame in their own pride?

And if it is a care you would cast off, that care has been chosen by you rather than imposed upon you.

And if it is a fear you would dispel, the seat of that fear is in your heart and not in the hand of the feared.

Verily all things move within your being in constant half embrace, the desired and the dreaded, the repugnant and the cherished, the pursued and that which you would escape.

These things move within you as lights and shadows in pairs that cling.

And when the shadow fades and is no more, the light that lingers becomes a shadow to another light.

And thus your freedom when it loses its fetters becomes itself the fetter of a greater freedom.   *P*, 61–4

THE PROPHET ON REASON
AND PASSION

Your soul is oftentimes a battlefield, upon which your reason and your judgement wage war against your passion and your appetite.

Would that I could be the peacemaker in your soul, that I might turn the discord and the rivalry of your elements into oneness and melody.

But how shall I, unless you yourselves be also the peacemakers, nay, the lovers of all your elements?

Your reason and your passion are the rudder and the sails of your seafaring soul.

If either your sails or your rudder be broken, you can but toss and drift, or else be held at a standstill in mid-seas.

For reason, ruling alone, is a force confining; and passion, unattended, is a flame that burns to its own destruction.

Therefore let your soul exalt your reason to the height of passion, that it may sing;

And let it direct your passion with reason, that your passion may live through its own daily resurrection, and like the phoenix rise above its own ashes.

I would have you consider your judgement and your appetite even as you would two loved guests in your house.

Surely you would not honour one guest above the

other; for he who is more mindful of one loses the love and the faith of both.

Among the hills, when you sit in the cool shade of the white poplars, sharing the peace and serenity of distant fields and meadows – then let your heart say in silence, 'God rests in reason.'

And when the storm comes, and the mighty wind shakes the forest, and thunder and lightning proclaim the majesty of the sky, then let your heart say in awe, 'God moves in passion.'

And since you are a breath in God's sphere, and a leaf in God's forest, you too should rest in reason and move in passion.   *P*, 65–7

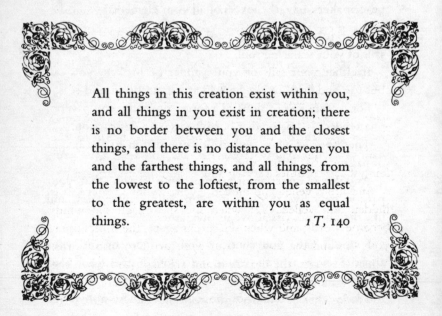

All things in this creation exist within you, and all things in you exist in creation; there is no border between you and the closest things, and there is no distance between you and the farthest things, and all things, from the lowest to the loftiest, from the smallest to the greatest, are within you as equal things.   *1 T*, 140

THE PROPHET ON LIFE

Life is older than all things living; even as beauty was winged ere the beautiful was born on earth, and even as truth was truth ere it was uttered.

Life sings in our silences, and dreams in our slumber. Even when we are beaten and low, life is enthroned and high. And when we weep, life smiles upon the day, and is free even when we drag our chains.

Oftentimes we call life bitter names, but only when we ourselves are bitter and dark. And we deem her empty and unprofitable, but only when the soul goes wandering in desolate places, and the heart is drunken with overmindfulness of self.

Life is deep and high and distant; and though only your vast vision can reach even her feet, yet she is near; and though only the breath of your breath reaches her heart, the shadow of your shadow crosses her face, and the echo of your faintest cry becomes a spring and an autumn in her breast.

And life is veiled and hidden, even as your greater self is hidden and veiled. Yet when life speaks, all the winds become words; and when she speaks again, the smiles upon your lips and the tears in your eyes turn also into words. When she sings, the deaf hear and are held; and when she comes walking, the sightless behold her and are amazed and follow her in wonder and astonishment.   *GP*, 9–10

PITY THE NATION

Pity the nation that wears a cloth it does not weave, eats a bread it does not harvest, and drinks a wine that flows not from its own winepress.

Pity the nation that acclaims the bully as hero, and that deems the glittering conqueror bountiful.

Pity the nation that despises a passion in its dream, yet submits in its awakening.

Pity the nation that raises not its voice save when it walks in a funeral, boasts not except among its ruins, and will rebel not save when its neck is laid between the sword and the block.

Pity the nation whose statesman is a fox, whose philosopher is a juggler, and whose art is the art of patching and mimicking.

Pity the nation that welcomes its new ruler with trumpetings, and farewells him with hootings, only to welcome another with trumpetings again.

Pity the nation whose sages are dumb with years and whose strong men are yet in the cradle.

Pity the nation divided into fragments, each fragment deeming itself a nation.   *GP*, 14–15

THE ECOLOGY OF LIFE

And then Mannus, the inquisitive disciple, looked about him and he saw plants in flower cleaving unto the sycamore tree. And he said: 'Behold the parasites, master. What say you of them? They are thieves with weary eyelids who steal the light from the steadfast children of the sun, and make fair of the sap that runneth into their branches and their leaves.'

And he answered him saying: 'My friend, we are all parasites. We who labour to turn the sod into pulsing life are not above those who receive life directly from the sod without knowing the sod.

'Shall a mother say to her child: "I give you back to the forest, which is your greater mother, for you weary me, heart and hand"?

'Or shall the singer rebuke his own song, saying: "Return now to the cave of echoes from whence you came, for your voice consumes my breath"?

'And shall the shepherd say to his yearling: "I have no pasture whereunto I may lead you; therefore be cut off and become a sacrifice for this cause"?

'Nay, my friend, all these things are answered even before they are asked, and, like your dreams, are fulfilled ere you sleep.

'We live upon one another according to the law, ancient

and timeless. Let us live thus in loving-kindness. We seek one another in our aloneness, and we walk the road when we have no hearth to sit beside.

'My friends and my brothers, the wider road is your fellow man.

'These plants that live upon the tree draw the milk of the earth in the sweet stillness of night, and the earth in her tranquil dreaming sucks at the breast of the sun.

'And the sun, even as you and I and all there is, sits in equal honour at the banquet of the prince whose door is always open and whose board is always spread.

'Mannus, my friend, all there is lives always upon all there is; and all there is lives in the faith, shoreless, upon the bounty of the Most High.'   *GP*, 29–31

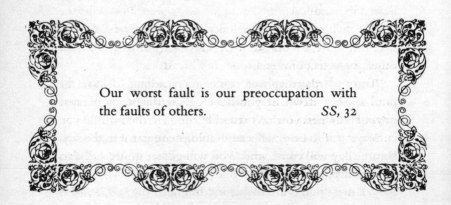

Our worst fault is our preoccupation with
the faults of others.   *SS*, 32

EVERYTHING IS ALIVE

And on a day, as Phardrous, the Greek, walked in the garden, he struck his foot upon a stone and he was angered. And he turned and picked up the stone, saying in a low voice: 'O dead thing in my path!' and he flung away the stone.

And Almustafa, the chosen and the beloved, said: 'Why say you: "O dead thing"? Have you been thus long in this garden and know not that there is nothing dead here? All things live and glow in the knowledge of the day and the majesty of the night. You and the stone are one. There is a difference only in heartbeats. Your heart beats a little faster, does it, my friend? Ay, but it is not so tranquil.

'Its rhythm may be another rhythm, but I say unto you that if you sound the depths of your soul and scale the heights of space, you shall hear but one melody, and in that melody the stone and the star sing, the one with the other, in perfect unison.

'If my words reach not your understanding, then let be until another dawn. If you have cursed this stone because in your blindness you have stumbled upon it, then would you curse a star if so be your head should encounter it in the sky. But the day will come when you will gather stones and stars as a child plucks the valley-lilies, and then shall you know that all these things are living and fragrant.'   *GP*, 36–7

THE PROPHET ON GOD

And on the first day of the week when the sounds of the temple bells sought their ears, one spoke and said: 'Master, we hear much talk of God hereabout. What say you of God, and who is He in very truth?'

And he stood before them like a young tree, fearless of wind or tempest, and he answered, saying: 'Think now, my comrades and beloved, of a heart that contains all your hearts, a love that encompasses all your loves, a spirit that envelops all your spirits, a voice enfolding all your voices, and a silence deeper than all your silences, and timeless.

'Seek now to perceive in your selffulness a beauty more enchanting than all things beautiful, a song more vast than the songs of the sea and the forest, a majesty seated upon a throne for which Orion is but a footstool, holding a sceptre in which the Pleiades are naught save the glimmer of dewdrops.

'You have sought always only food and shelter, a garment and a staff; seek now one who is neither an aim for your arrows nor a stony cave to shield you from the elements.

'And if my words are a rock and a riddle, then seek, none the less, that your hearts may be broken, and that your questionings may bring you unto the love and the wisdom of the Most High, whom men call God.'

And they were silent, every one, and they were perplexed

in their heart; and Almustafa was moved with compassion for them, and he gazed with tenderness upon them and said: 'Let us speak no more now of God the Father. Let us speak rather of the gods, your neighbours, and of your brothers, the elements that move about your houses and your fields.

'You would rise in fancy unto the cloud, and you deem it height; and you would pass over the vast sea and claim it to be distance. But I say unto you that when you sow a seed in the earth, you reach a greater height; and when you hail the beauty of the morning to your neighbour, you cross a greater sea.

'Too often do you sing God, the infinite, and yet in truth you hear not the song. Would that you might listen to the songbirds, and to the leaves that forsake the branch when the wind passes by, and forget not, my friends, that these sing only when they are separated from the branch!

'Again I bid you to speak not so freely of God, who is your all, but speak rather and understand one another, neighbour unto neighbour, a god unto a god.

'For what shall feed the fledgling in the nest if the mother bird flies skywards? And what anemone in the field shall be fulfilled unless it be husbanded by a bee from another anemone?

'It is only when you are lost in your smaller selves that you seek the sky which you call God. Would that you might find paths into your vast selves; would that you might be less idle and pave the roads!

'My mariners and my friends, it were wiser to speak less of God, whom we cannot understand, and more of each other, whom we may understand. Yet I would have you know that we are the breath and the fragrance of God. We are God, in leaf, in flower, and oftentimes in fruit.'   *GP*, 38–41

PART FIVE

Christ and Christianity

Extracts from *Jesus the Son of Man*

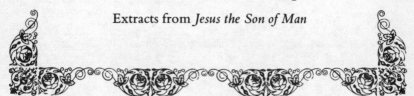

Once every hundred years Jesus of Nazareth meets Jesus of the Christian in a garden among the hills of Lebanon, and they talk long. And each time Jesus of Nazareth goes away saying to Jesus of the Christian,

'My friend, I fear we shall never, never agree.'

Sand and Foam, 77

MARY MAGDALEN

It was in the month of June when I saw Him for the first time. He was walking in the wheat field when I passed by with my handmaidens, and He was alone.

The rhythm of His step was different from other men's, and the movement of His body was like naught I had seen before.

Men do not pace the earth in that manner. And even now I do not know whether He walked fast or slow.

My handmaidens pointed their fingers at Him and spoke in shy whispers to one another. And I stayed my steps for a moment, and raised my hand to hail Him. But He did not turn His face, and He did not look at me. And I hated Him. I was swept back into myself, and I was as cold as if I had been in a snowdrift. And I shivered.

That night I beheld Him in my dreaming; and they told me afterwards that I screamed in my sleep and was restless upon my bed.

It was in the month of August that I saw Him again, through my window. He was sitting in the shadow of the cypress tree across my garden, and He was as still as if He had been carved out of stone, like the statues in Antioch and other cities of the North Country.

And my slave, the Egyptian, came to me and said, 'That man is here again. He is sitting there across your garden.'

And I gazed at Him, and my soul quivered within me, for He was beautiful.

His body was single and each part seemed to love every other part.

Then I clothed myself with raiment of Damascus, and I left my house and walked towards Him.

Was it my aloneness, or was it His fragrance, that drew me to Him? Was it a hunger in my eyes that desired comeliness, or was it His beauty that sought the light of my eyes?

Even now I do not know.

I walked to Him with my scented garments and my golden sandals, the sandals the Roman captain had given me, even these sandals. And when I reached Him, I said, 'Good-morrow to you.'

And He said, 'Good-morrow to you, Miriam.'

And He looked at me, and His night-eyes saw me as no man had seen me. And suddenly I was as if naked, and I was shy.

Yet He had only said, 'Good-morrow to you.'

And then I said to Him, 'Will you not come to my house?'

And He said, 'Am I not already in your house?'

I did not know what He meant then, but I know now.

And I said, 'Will you not have wine and bread with me?'

And He said, 'Yes, Miriam, but not now.'

Not now, *not now*, He said. And the voice of the sea was in those two words, and the voice of the wind and the trees. And when He said them unto me, life spoke to death.

For mind you, my friend, I was dead. I was a woman

who had divorced her soul. I was living apart from this self which you now see. I belonged to all men, and to none. They called me harlot, and a woman possessed of seven devils. I was cursed, and I was envied.

But when His dawn-eyes looked into my eyes all the stars of my night faded away, and I became Miriam, only Miriam, a woman lost to the earth she had known, and finding herself in new places.

And now again I said to Him, 'Come into my house and share bread and wine with me.'

And He said, 'Why do you bid me to be your guest?'

And I said, 'I beg you to come into my house.' And it was all that was sod in me, and all that was sky in me calling unto Him.

Then He looked at me, and the noontide of His eyes was upon me, and He said, 'You have many lovers, and yet I alone love you. Other men love themselves in your nearness. I love you in yourself. Other men see a beauty in you that shall fade away sooner than their own years. But I see in you a beauty that shall not fade away, and in the autumn of your days that beauty shall not be afraid to gaze at itself in the mirror, and it shall not be offended.

'I alone love the unseen in you.'

Then He said in a low voice, 'Go away now. If this cypress tree is yours and you would not have me sit in its shadow, I will walk my way.'

And I cried to Him and I said, 'Master, come to my house. I have incense to burn for you, and a silver basin for your feet. You are a stranger and yet not a stranger. I entreat you, come to my house.'

Then He stood up and looked at me even as the seasons might look down upon the field, and He smiled. And He said again: 'All men love you for themselves. I love you for yourself.'

And then He walked away.

But no other man ever walked the way He walked. Was it a breath born in my garden that moved to the east? Or was it a storm that would shake all things to their foundations?

I knew not, but on that day the sunset of His eyes slew the dragon in me, and I became a woman, I became Miriam, Miriam of Mijdel.   *JSM*, 12–15

LUKE

Jesus despised and scorned the hypocrites, and His wrath was like a tempest that scourged them. His voice was thunder in their ears and He cowed them.

In their fear of Him they sought His death; and like moles in the dark earth they worked to undermine His footsteps. But He fell not into their snares.

He laughed at them, for well He knew that the spirit shall not be mocked, nor shall it be taken in the pitfall.

He held a mirror in His hand and therein He saw the sluggard and the limping and those who stagger and fall by the roadside on the way to the summit.

And He pitied them all. He would even have raised them to His stature and He would have carried their burden. Nay, He would have bid their weakness lean on His strength.

He did not utterly condemn the liar or the thief or the murderer, but He did utterly condemn the hypocrite whose face is masked and whose hand is gloved.

Often have I pondered on the heart that shelters all who come from the wasteland to its sanctuary, yet against the hypocrite is closed and sealed.

On a day as we rested with Him in the Garden of Pomegranates, I said to Him, 'Master, you forgive and console the sinner and all the weak and the infirm save only the hypocrite alone.'

And He said, 'You have chosen your words well when you called sinners weak and infirm. I do forgive them their weakness of body and their infirmity of spirit. For their failings have been laid upon them by their forefathers, or by the greed of their neighbours.

'But I tolerate not the hypocrite, because he himself lays a yoke upon the guileless and the yielding.

'Weaklings, whom you call sinners, are like the featherless young that fall from the nest. The hypocrite is the vulture waiting upon a rock for the death of the prey.

'Weaklings are men lost in a desert. But the hypocrite is not lost. He knows the way, yet he laughs between the sand and the wind.

'For this cause I do not receive him.'

Thus our master spoke, and I did not understand. But I understand now.

Then the hypocrites of the land laid hands upon Him and they judged Him; and in so doing they deemed themselves justified. For they cited the law of Moses in the Sanhedrin in witness and evidence against Him.

And they who break the law at the rise of every dawn and break it again at sunset, brought about His death.   *JSM*, 35–6

NATHANIEL

They say that Jesus of Nazareth was humble and meek.

They say that though He was a just man and righteous, He was a weakling, and was often confounded by the strong and the powerful; and that when He stood before men of authority He was but a lamb among lions.

But I say that Jesus had authority over men, and that He knew His power and proclaimed it among the hills of Galilee, and in the cities of Judaea and Phoenicia.

What man yielding and soft would say, 'I am life, and I am the way to truth'?

What man meek and lowly would say, 'I am in God, our Father; and our God, the Father, is in me'?

What man unmindful of His own strength would say, 'He who believes not in me believes not in this life nor in the life everlasting'?

What man uncertain of tomorrow would proclaim, 'Your world shall pass away and be naught but scattered ashes ere my words shall pass away'?

Was He doubtful of Himself when He said to those who would confound Him with a harlot, 'He who is without sin, let him cast a stone'?

Did He fear authority when He drove the money-changers from the court of the temple, though they were licensed by the priests?

Were His wings shorn when He cried aloud, 'My kingdom is above your earthly kingdoms'?

Was He seeking shelter in words when He repeated again and yet again, 'Destroy this temple and I will rebuild it in three days'?

Was it a coward who shook His hand in the face of the authorities and pronounced them 'Liars, low, filthy, and degenerate'?

Shall a man bold enough to say these things to those who ruled Judaea be deemed meek and humble?

Nay. The eagle builds not his nest in the weeping willow. And the lion seeks not his den among the ferns.

I am sickened and the bowels within me stir and rise when I hear the faint-hearted call Jesus humble and meek, that they may justify their own faint-heartedness; and when the downtrodden, for comfort and companionship, speak of Jesus as a worm shining by their side.

Yea, my heart is sickened by such men. It is the mighty hunter I would preach, and the mountainous spirit unconquerable. *JSM*, 59–60

SABA OF ANTIOCH

This day I heard Saul of Tarsus preaching the Christ unto the Jews of this city.

He calls himself Paul now, the apostle to the Gentiles.

I knew him in my youth, and in those days he persecuted the friends of the Nazarene. Well do I remember his satisfaction when his fellows stoned the radiant youth called Stephen.

This Paul is indeed a strange man. His soul is not the soul of a free man.

At times he seems like an animal in the forest, hunted and wounded, seeking a cave wherein he would hide his pain from the world.

He speaks not of Jesus, nor does he repeat His words. He preaches the Messiah whom the prophets of old had foretold.

And though he himself is a learned Jew he addresses his fellow Jews in Greek; and his Greek is halting, and he ill chooses his words.

But he is a man of hidden powers and his presence is affirmed by those who gather round him. And at times he assures them of what he himself is not assured.

We who knew Jesus and heard His discourses say that He taught man how to break the chains of his bondage that he might be free from his yesterdays.

But Paul is forging chains for the man of tomorrow. He would strike with his own hammer upon the anvil in the name of one whom he does not know.

The Nazarene would have us live the hour in passion and ecstasy.

The man of Tarsus would have us be mindful of laws recorded in the ancient books.

Jesus gave His breath to the breathless dead. And in my lone nights I believe and I understand.

When He sat at the board, He told stories that gave happiness to the feasters, and spiced with His joy the meat and the wine.

But Paul would prescribe our loaf and our cup.

Suffer me now to turn my eyes the other way.

JSM, 61–2

CLEOPAS OF BETHROUNE

When Jesus spoke the whole world was hushed to listen. His words were not for our ears but rather for the elements of which God made this earth.

He spoke to the sea, our vast mother, that gave us birth. He spoke to the mountain, our elder brother whose summit is a promise.

And He spoke to the angels beyond the sea and the mountain to whom we entrusted our dreams ere the clay in us was made hard in the sun.

And still His speech slumbers within our breast like a love-song half forgotten, and sometimes it burns itself through to our memory.

His speech was simple and joyous, and the sound of His voice was like cool water in a land of drought.

Once He raised His hand against the sky, and His fingers were like the branches of a sycamore tree; and He said with a great voice:

'The prophets of old have spoken to you, and your ears are filled with their speech. But I say unto you, empty your ears of what you have heard.'

And these words of Jesus, '*But I say unto you,*' were not uttered by a man of our race nor of our world; but rather by a host of seraphim marching across the sky of Judaea.

Again and yet again He would quote the law and

the prophets, and then He would say, '*But I say unto you.*'

Oh, what burning words, what waves of seas unknown to the shores of our mind, '*But I say unto you.*'

What stars seeking the darkness of the soul, and what sleepless souls awaiting the dawn.

To tell of the speech of Jesus one must needs have His speech or the echo thereof.

I have neither the speech nor the echo.

I beg you to forgive me for beginning a story that I cannot end. But the end is not yet upon my lips. It is still a love song in the wind. *JSM,* 70–71

A PHILOSOPHER

When He was with us He gazed at us and at our world with eyes of wonder, for His eyes were not veiled with the veil of years, and all that He saw was clear in the light of His youth.

Though He knew the depth of beauty, He was for ever surprised by its peace and its majesty; and He stood before the earth as the first man had stood before the first day.

We whose senses have been dulled, we gaze in full daylight and yet we do not see. We would cup our ears, but we do not hear; and stretch forth our hands, but we do not touch. And though all the incense of Arabia is burned, we go our way and do not smell.

We see not the ploughman returning from his field at eventide; nor hear the shepherd's flute when he leads his flock to the fold; nor do we stretch our arms to touch the sunset; and our nostrils hunger no longer for the roses of Sharon.

Nay, we honour no kings without kingdoms; nor hear the sound of harps save when the strings are plucked by hands; nor do we see a child playing in our olive grove as if he were a young olive tree. And all words must needs rise from lips of flesh, or else we deem each other dumb and deaf.

In truth we gaze but do not see, and hearken but do not

hear; we eat and drink but do not taste. And there lies the difference between Jesus of Nazareth and ourselves.

His senses were all continually made new, and the world to Him was always a new world.

To Him the lisping of a babe was not less than the cry of all mankind, while to us it is only lisping.

To Him the root of a buttercup was a longing towards God, while to us it is naught but a root.   *JSM*, 96–7

JOSEPH OF ARIMATHEA

There were two streams running in the heart of the Nazarene: the stream of kinship to God whom He called Father, and the stream of rapture which He called the kingdom of the above-world.

And in my solitude I thought of Him and I followed these two streams in His heart. Upon the banks of the one I met my own soul; and sometimes my soul was a beggar and a wanderer, and sometimes it was a princess in her garden.

Then I followed the other stream in His heart, and on my way I met one who had been beaten and robbed of his gold, and he was smiling. And farther on I saw the robber who had robbed him, and there were unshed tears upon his face.

Then I heard the murmur of these two streams in my own bosom also, and I was gladdened.

When I visited Jesus the day before Pontius Pilatus and the elders laid hands on Him, we talked long, and I asked Him many questions, and He answered my questionings with graciousness; and when I left Him I knew He was the Lord and master of this our earth.

It is long since the cedar tree has fallen, but its fragrance endures, and will for ever seek the four corners of the earth. *JSM*, 104

JOSEPH SURNAMED JUSTUS

They say He was vulgar, the common offspring of common seed, a man uncouth and violent.

They say that only the wind combed His hair, and only the rain brought His clothes and His body together.

They deem Him mad, and they attribute His words to demons.

Yet behold, the Man despised sounded a challenge and the sound thereof shall never cease.

He sang a song and none shall arrest that melody. It shall hover from generation to generation and it shall rise from sphere to sphere remembering the lips that gave it birth and the ears that cradled it.

He was a stranger. Aye, He was a stranger, a wayfarer on His way to a shrine, a visitor who knocked at our door, a guest from a far country.

And because He found not a gracious host, He has returned to His own place.   *JSM*, 168

EVENTIDE OF THE FEAST

Night had fallen and obscurity engulfed the city while the lights glittered in the palaces and the huts and the shops. The multitudes, wearing their festive raiment, crowded the streets and upon their faces appeared the signs of celebration and contentment.

I avoided the clamour of the throngs and walked alone, contemplating the man whose greatness they were honouring, and meditating the genius of the ages who was born in poverty, and lived virtuously, and died on the cross.

I was pondering the burning torch which was lighted in this humble village in Syria by the Holy Spirit. The Holy Spirit who hovers over all the ages, and penetrates one civilization and then another through His truth.

As I reached the public garden, I seated myself on a rustic bench and commenced looking between the naked trees towards the crowded streets; I listened to the hymns and songs of the celebrants.

After an hour of deep thinking, I looked sidewise and was surprised to find a man sitting by me, holding a short branch with which he engraved vague figures on the ground. I was startled, for I had not seen nor heard his approach, but I said within myself, 'He is solitary, as I am.' And after looking thoroughly at him, I saw that in spite of his old-fashioned raiment and long hair, he was a dignified man, worthy of attention. It seemed that he detected the thoughts within me, for in a deep and quiet voice he said, 'Good evening, my son.'

'Good evening to you,' I responded with respect.

And he resumed his drawing while the strangely soothing sound of his voice was still echoing in my ears. And I spoke to him again, saying, 'Are you a stranger in this city?'

'Yes, I am a stranger in this city and every city,' he replied. I consoled him, adding, 'A stranger should forget that he is an outsider in these holidays, for there is kindness and generosity in the people.' He replied wearily, 'I am more a stranger in these days than in any other.' Having thus spoken, he looked at the clear skies; his eyes probed the stars and his lips quivered as if he had found in the firmament an image of a distant country. His queer statement aroused my interest, and I said, 'This is the time of the year when the people are kind to all other people. The rich remember the poor and the strong have compassion for the weak.'

He returned, 'Yes, the momentary mercy of the rich upon the poor is bitter, and the sympathy of the strong towards the weak is naught but a reminder of superiority.'

I affirmed, 'Your words have merit, but the weak poor do not care to know what transpires in the heart of the rich, and the hungry never think of the method by which the bread he is craving is kneaded and baked.'

And he responded, 'The one who receives is not mindful, but the one who gives bears the burden of cautioning himself that it is with a view to brotherly love, and towards friendly aid, and not to self-esteem.'

I was amazed at his wisdom, and again commenced to

meditate upon his ancient appearance and strange garments. Then I returned mentally and said, 'It appears that you are in need of help; will you accept a few coins from me?' And with a sad smile he answered me, saying, 'Yes, I am in desperate need, but not of gold or silver.'

Puzzled, I asked, 'What is it that you require?'

'I am in need of shelter. I am in need of a place where I can rest my head and my thoughts.'

'Please accept these two dinars and go to the inn for lodging,' I insisted.

Sorrowfully he answered, 'I have tried every inn, and knocked at every door, but in vain. I have entered every food shop, but none cared to help me. I am hurt, not hungry; I am disappointed, not tired; I seek not a roof, but human shelter.'

I said within myself, 'What a strange person he is! Once he talks like a philosopher and again like a madman!' As I whispered these thoughts into the ears of my inner self, he stared at me, lowered his voice to a sad level, and said, 'Yes, I am a madman, but even a madman will find himself a stranger without shelter and hungry without food, for the heart of man is empty.'

I apologized to him, saying, 'I regret my unwitting thought. Would you accept my hospitality and take shelter in my quarters?'

'I knocked at your door and all the doors one thousand times, and received no answer,' he answered severely.

Now I was convinced that he was truly a madman, and I suggested, 'Let us go now, and proceed to my home.'

He lifted his head slowly and said, 'If you were aware of my identity you would not invite me to your home.'

'Who are you?' I inquired, fearfully, slowly.

With a voice that sounded like the roar of the ocean, he thundered, bitterly, 'I am the revolution who builds what the nations destroy. I am the tempest who uproots the plants, grown by the ages. I am the one who came to spread war on earth and not peace, for man is content only in misery!'

And, with tears coursing down his cheeks, he stood up high, and a mist of light grew about him, and he stretched forth his arms, and I saw the marks of the nails in the palms of his hands; I prostrated myself before him convulsively and cried out, saying, 'Oh Jesus, the Nazarene!'

And He continued, in anguish, 'The people are celebrating in my honour, pursuing the tradition woven by the ages around my name, but as to myself, I am a stranger wandering from east to west upon this earth, and no one knows of me. The foxes have their holes, and the birds of the skies their nests, but the Son of Man has no place to rest His head.'

At that moment, I opened my eyes, lifted my head, and looked around, but found naught except a column of smoke before me, and I heard only the shivering voice of the silence of the night, coming from the depths of eternity. I collected myself and looked again to the singing throngs in the distance, and a voice within me said, 'The very strength that protects the heart from injury is the strength that prevents the heart from enlarging to its intended greatness within. The song of the voice is sweet, but the song of the heart is the pure voice of heaven.'

1T, 117–21